Mountain Plants of Northeastern Utah

by

Berniece A. Andersen

and

Arthur H. Holmgren

CONTENTS

Cooperative Extension Work in Agriculture and Home Economics, William H. Bennett, Director. Utah State University of Agriculture and Applied Science and the United States Department of Agriculture, Cooperating. Distributed in furtherance of Acts of Congress of May 8 and June 30, 1914. (2.5M/11-69/CPN)

PURPOSE AND DESCRIPTION OF THIS MANUAL

It has been our purpose to prepare a guide which will be of use to students, amateur botanists and laymen interested in the wildflowers of a rather limited geographical area. Taxonomists have classified nearly 3000 species from the Bear River, Wasatch, and Uinta Mountains. We have limited ourselves to a representative selection of the more common, conspicuous or beautiful species and have deliberately excluded many of the less attractive or weedy plants, even though they may be common, since they have only limited interest to the non-professional botanist. Grasses have not been treated here, since they have been so well treated in John Valentine's bulletin, *Important Utah Range Grasses*, Extension Circular 281. It is our hope that this will serve as a handbook for field identification and as a classroom reference. There are 351 illustrations, together with a brief description of each. Fifty-eight more plants are identified by comparative description.

We have arranged the plants in their natural family groups and have identified each with its most popular common name or names, as well as its scientific name.

We are chiefly concerned with family, genus, and species. Only a few sub-species and varieties are mentioned. No attempt has been made to include authors of scientific names.

We have included a basic illustrated vocabulary list and glossary in the front of the manual. An index of common and scientific names concludes the work.

ACKNOWLEDGEMENTS

In gathering our information we have leaned heavily upon the work of many taxonomists and botanical writers. To them we gratefully acknowledge our indebtedness.

We also wish to express our gratitude to Dr. W. S. Boyle and Dr. J. S. Williams for their suggestions on the introduction; to Dr. G. E. Bohart and the young Andersens for supplying much of the fresh plant material used in making the drawings; to Dr. S. G. Ellsworth for maps of the area and to all others who have offered their encouragement and assistance.

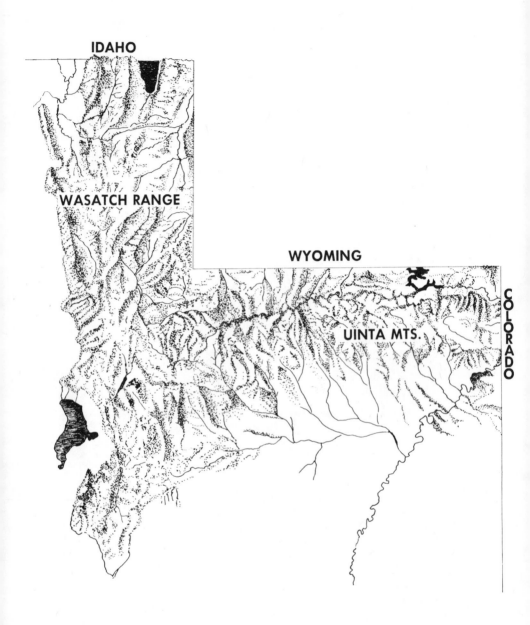

IDAHO

WASATCH RANGE

WYOMING

UINTA MTS.

COLORADO

Landforms Maps of Northeastern Utah

INTRODUCTION

Location

The area covered in this guide is in the mountainous regions in the northeast corners of our state. It includes the Wasatch, Bear River and Uinta Mountains.

The Wasatch and Bear River Mountains

The Wasatch Mountains trend north and south for nearly 200 miles from the Wellsville Mountains to Mount Nebo on the south. They mark our eastern border with Wyoming and are the western front of the Middle Rocky Mountains. The Bear River Mountains extend from Jones Peak northeast of Ogden to the great bend near Soda Springs, Idaho.

The elevations of the Wasatch Mountains range between 4,200 and 11,957 feet (at Mount Timpanogos). Their crest is generally above 10,000 feet. The Bear River Mountains are a little lower.

The most striking characteristic of the Wasatch Mountains is their abrupt, wall-like western front cut by deep canyons. This front once was a shoreline of Lake Bonneville.

The Uinta Mountains

The Uinta Range is approximately 150 miles long and 40 miles wide. Its elevation is generally higher than the Wasatch Range. It has many peaks and crests above 12,000 feet and numerous ridges at only slightly lower altitudes. Its highest peak (King's Peak) is 13,498 feet.

Rivers

Three large rivers, the Provo, the Bear, and the Weber, which begin in the Uinta Mountains, discharge into the Great Salt Lake. The Green River joins the Colorado and eventually flows into the Pacific Ocean. Numerous smaller streams flow from the canyons.

Environment

Scattered across the vast terrain there are more than a thousand sparkling, jewel-like lakes (gouged out by the glaciers that once covered the area). Both ranges have pockets of lush green mountain meadow and areas of alpine tundra; that is, terrain above the tree line, where vegetation is dwarfed by harsh climate and short growing season.

Climate differences produce a broad seasonal spread. Roughly speaking, for every 1,000 feet of elevation, there is a drop in temperature of three Fahrenheit degrees. Going up 1,000 feet is roughly equivalent to going north 3000 miles at sea level. This means that the same species of flower which blooms about April 15th at 5,000 feet may bloom about July 1st at 8,000 feet. This is dramatically illustrated in many of our Utah wildflower areas.

Soil differences correspond generally to the basic rock types and the amount of rainfall for a specific area.

The Bear River Range and the Wasatch Mountains at the northern end of Utah are made up principally of limestone and dolomite rocks while the Uintas are largely granite. Soils of widely varying chemical composition are found throughout the area, thus providing a suitable environment for plants requiring acid soil as well as those that need lime.

Rainfall, which is profoundly influenced by mountains, varies between 20 and 40 inches. This, together with variations in wind currents, elevation, drainage, soil, etc., produces an infinite variety of growing conditions within a relatively short distance.

These variations of terrain and climate result in our having some of the most diversified, florid, and beautiful areas in the world.

Adaptability

Generally speaking, in the struggle for survival, those plants succeed best that are best equipped genetically to cope with the prevailing conditions of their environment.

In the mountains, these conditions are diverse and constantly changing. Frequently, vagaries of the season produce irregularities such as a short or extremely dry season. Were it not for the breadth of plant adaption, such occurrences would eliminate whole areas of plant life. As it is, the types of plants growing there change, but rarely disappear.

The mechanisms involved in adaption are truly marvelous. In dry areas, many plants have wide spreading root systems that absorb maximum amounts of water whenever it is available or deep roots that tap moisture after shallow moisture is gone. Some leaves and stems are equipped to preserve precious moisture within the plant. Other plants may adjust to a dry season by producing early blossoms that will develop seed in a very short period of time.

Often plants growing at high altitudes, where the snow drifts remain until late in the season, generate enough heat to melt out small pockets in the snow. There they develop leaves and are ready to bloom as soon as the snow disappears.

In inclement weather, some plants simply stop development until it "warms up" and then proceed with their cycle. Hot, dry weather speeds the process to fit the need.

Variation

Within any species there are genetic variations. This paves the way for adaptive changes within a group of plants and increases the chances for survival of the species when they are confronted with drastic changes or hazards in their environment. The plants least adapted to meeting a particular crisis are destroyed, while others within the species survive. These, in turn, produce plants with characteristics like their own and the species takes a step in evolution.

Plants differ greatly from each other. We become accustomed to thinking of plants as being self-supporting, with roots that grow into the earth and leaves and flowers that grow on stems. Yet many plants do not fit this pattern. Some are parasitic, deriving their nourishment partially or totally from a host plant. Others do not have what we think of as common plant characteristics.

Within the plant kingdom one finds constant surprises. It is a fabulous world of inexhaustible discovery.

Getting to Know Your Wildflowers

Getting to know our flora is important in the total enjoyment of our out-of-doors. As our knowledge of plants increases, it becomes part of the marvelous tapestry of related environmental factors, and we pursue each season with more zest in exploration, memory and expectation.

Our pleasure in individual plants, too, increases as we know them. The cinquefoil becomes more interesting when we associate it with the rose family and realize that it bears resemblance to other members of its family.

We are reminded of our ties with the past and with the rest of the world, when we realize that our familiar uncultivated flora is made up of introduced plants as well as of those native to our soil.

With our Western pioneers came many of their favorite plants, while explorers, botanists and travelers eagerly sought out new and different plants to take or send to Europe.

A great many of these introduced plants have found their new environment hospitable and have become widely naturalized.

IDENTIFICATION BY NAMES

Although a great many common names are picturesque and descriptive, they do a poor job of identifying plants. These names vary widely from one locality to another, and any single plant may have several current and equally valid common names. At the same time, completely unrelated plants may bear the same name. The need for an accurate definitive name for each plant is apparent. This is accomplished by a system of grouping which is remarkably logical and simple when one understands it. The divisions of classification are as follows:

Class
Order
Family
Genus
Species
Subspecies
Variety

Introduction

Scientific names are made up of two parts: The generic name (genus) and the specific name (species), in that order. They have come from many sources. Some originated with the ancient Greeks. Most, however, have a history of only a few hundred years. Some of our western plant names are less than a decade old. The western colonizing era (between 1800 and 1875) was a period of extensive activity by plant explorers. As a memoriam to their contributions of early botanical discovery, scores of scientific plant names are Latinized versions of such names as Lewis, Clark, Pursh, Wyeth, Douglas, Parry, Kellogg, Gambel and Nuttall, to mention only a few. Other plant names are in some way descriptive of some characteristics of the plant.

Now and in the Future

By knowing our wildflowers we can better preserve them for ourselves and for the future.

Wildflowers are often abundant, but they are not indestructable — many of our loveliest ones are in danger of extinction by our carelessness. This need not happen if we observe the following rules of courtesy:

1. Do not pick the wildflowers. Enjoy them and leave them for someone else to enjoy. They are perishable and have a very short "indoor" life; also, with many of them, roots as well as seeds are killed when the flowers are picked.

2. Do not try to transplant them into your garden. Almost without exception, they do not tolerate root disturbance. Your chances of success in raising them domestically are far greater if you begin with seed. Even so, many of them need soil, temperature and other conditions not available outside of their immediate environment.

3. Be respectful of them in their natural environment. Do not injure them with fire, tramping or other thoughtless acts.

PICTURE GLOSSARY

THE VOCABULARY DESCRIBING FLOWERING PLANT CHARACTERISTICS

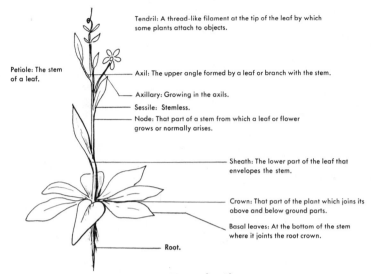

Tendril: A thread-like filament at the tip of the leaf by which some plants attach to objects.

Petiole: The stem of a leaf.

Axil: The upper angle formed by a leaf or branch with the stem.

Axillary: Growing in the axils.

Sessile: Stemless.

Node: That part of a stem from which a leaf or flower grows or normally arises.

Sheath: The lower part of the leaf that envelopes the stem.

Crown: That part of the plant which joins its above and below ground parts.

Basal leaves: At the bottom of the stem where it joints the root crown.

Root.

Parts of a Plant

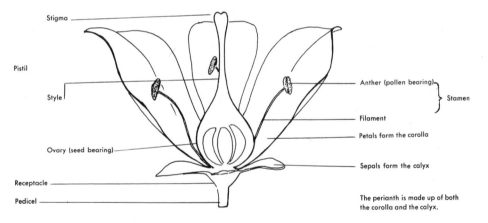

Stigma

Pistil

Style

Ovary (seed bearing)

Receptacle

Pedicel

Anther (pollen bearing)

Stamen

Filament

Petals form the corolla

Sepals form the calyx

The perianth is made up of both the corolla and the calyx.

Parts of a Flower

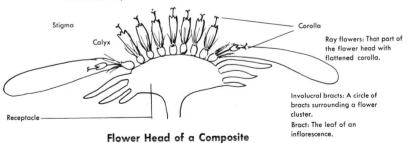

Disk flowers: That part of the flower head bearing small tubular corollas.

Stigma

Calyx

Corolla

Ray flowers: That part of the flower head with flattened corolla.

Involucral bracts: A circle of bracts surrounding a flower cluster.

Bract: The leaf of an inflorescence.

Receptacle

Flower Head of a Composite

FLOWERS AND INFLORESCENCES

Separate petals.

Fused corolla.

Spurred: A spur is a hollow, tubular projection on a flower.

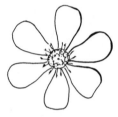

Regular flower radially symmetric.

Irregular flower bilaterally symmetric.

Spike: An elongated cluster of stockless flowers.

Catkin: The scaly spike or raceme of a bush or willow.

Panicle: A branching or compound raceme.

Raceme: An elongated flower cluster with single flowers on stems arranged along a stalk.

Scape

Terminal: Single blossom at the top of a stem or scape.

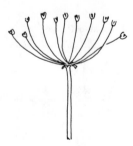

Umbel: A flower cluster in which all flower stalks arise from a common terminal point.

Compound umbel.

VARIATIONS IN LEAF SHAPE

Linear: Long and narrow with parellel sides.

Lanceolate: Much longer than wide and tapering upwards from the middle.

Oblong: Longer than broad with parallel sides.

Elliptical: Broadest in the middle, equally rounded at the ends.

Orbicular: Round.

Ovate: Egg-shaped, broadest near the base.

Obovate: Egg-shaped with broadest end at the top.

Cordate: Heart-shaped.

Deltoid: Triangular.

Sagittate.

Cunate.

Frond: The highly specialized leaf of a fern.

VARIATIONS IN LEAF MARGIN

Entire: The margin not in any way indented.

Crenate: Wavy margins.

Serrate: Toothed.

Lobed: Cut so as to leave prominent projections.

11

LEAVES
Leaf Arrangement

Simple leaf in one piece.

Petiole

Palmately compound: Spreading from the tip of the stem like fingers from the palm of a hand.

Pinnately compound: Leaflets arranged on both sides of the petiole.

Opposite: Two leaves to a node.

Whorl: A circle of leaves or flowers at the same joint or node.

Alternate: One leaf to a node.

ROOTS
Root Types

Fibrous: Made up of primary and secondary roots of about the same size.

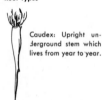

Caudex: Upright underground stem which lives from year to year.

Tap root: The primary root, which is much larger than the secondary roots.

Rootstock or rhizomes of grass: An underground, more or less horizontal stem.
Stolon: A horizontal stem usually at the surface of the ground.

Section of a bulb: A short thickened stem bearing many fleshy or scale-like leaves, as in Allium.

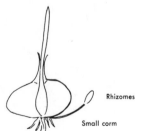

Rhizomes

Small corm

Section of a corm or solid bulb: A fleshy enlarged base of a stem with few or no scales.

Fleshy rhizome of an iris.

12

FRUIT

Fruit is the product of the ripened ovary or pistil with accessory parts.

Simple Achene

With hairy appendage for wind distribution

Barbed for animal distribution

Achene: A dry, hard, one seeded fruit, with or without appendages to aid in their distribution.

Winged for wind distribution

Follicle: A fruit with a single chamber opening on one side at maturity.

Capsule: A dry fruit of more than one carpel and opening at maturity.

Legume pod. The fruit of the Leguminosae. It splits open on two lines.

Nut: A one seeded fruit with thick hard shell which does not split open at maturity. It usually has two compartments.

Berry: A fruit with a pulpy pericarp. A pericarp is the ripened walls of the ovary.

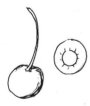

Drupe: A fruit with a fleshy outer coat covering a single seed.

Pome: An apple-like fruit.

Aggregate: A fruit from one flower crowded into a dense cluster but not joined.

COMMON BOTANICAL TERMS

Annual — A plant maturing and producing seed in one year.

Axillary — Borne at an axil.

Biennial — Of two years duration.

Bearded — With long or stiff hairs.

Bloom — A usually waxy whitish powder covering part of a plant.

Carpel — A modified leaf forming the ovary.

Chlorophyll — The green coloring matter of plants.

Corymb — A flat topped racemose in which the outermost flowers open first.

Cyme — A flat topped racemose in which the innermost flowers open first.

Decumbent — The base of the plant resting on the ground with the upper part rising.

Dicotyledons — Any plant having a double first or seed leaf.

Ecology — Study of habits and modes of life of plants and animals.

Exfoliating — Coming off in layers.

Gland — Small round bodies, sessile or on raised stalks that secrete some substance.

Glabrous — Smooth, without hair.

Glutinous — Sticky.

Herb — A plant with the above-ground stems living only one season.

Imperfect flower — Lacking either stamens or pistils.

Monocotyledons — Any plant having a single first or seed leaf.

Needles — The leaves of members of the pine family.

Panicle — A cluster of associated inflorescence.

Pappus — The plumose, bristle-like or scaly appendage on the seeds of members of the sunflower family.

Parasitic — Living on and deriving nourishment from other living organisms.

Perennial — A plant that lives for two or more years.

Perfect flower — Having both stamens and pistil.

Procumbent — Trailing on the ground.

Pubescent — Covered with hair.

Saprophyte — A plant living on dead organic matter.

Scape — A leafless flowering stem.

Shrub — A woody perennial without a trunk but with several main branches.

*   *   *   *

Transfer of the *pollen* from the *anther* to the *stigma* constitutes *pollination*. This is accomplished by insects (mostly bees), wind, animals or within the plant itself.

Fertilization, which is the fusion of sperm and egg, is necessary for seed development in most plants.

A few plants are an exception to this rule and develop seed without fertilization. This process is called *apomixis*.

Ferns and Fern Allies

FERN FAMILY

Although we have relatively few different kinds of ferns, they are among our most interesting and beautiful plants. Ferns do not have flowers and fruits but reproduce by spores, which can be seen on the under side of the leaves.

Fig. 1. Brittle Bladder Fern

BRITTLE BLADDER FERN

(*Cystopteris fragilis*), Fig. 1, is our most common fern. It rarely grows more than 8 inches tall and may be found in early spring in semi-shady moist places. Its delicate lacy fronds usually dry up in the summer but appear again the following spring.

Fig. 2. Lady Fern

LADY FERN (*Athyrium filix-femina*), Fig. 2, is similar, but larger, sometimes growing 3 feet tall. It grows in granitic soil by streams. This is the most beautiful of all our ferns. It is rather rare here, although it is quite common in less arid climates.

Fig. 3. Bracken Fern

BRACKEN FERN (*Pteridium aquilinum* var. *pubescens*), Fig. 3, is a rather coarse fern with leathery fronds that arise singly from underground rootstocks or grows in open woods where the soil is neutral or acid. *Pteridium* is a Greek word meaning coarse, stiff, and green.

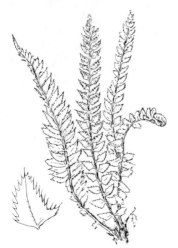

Fig. 4. Mountain Holly Fern

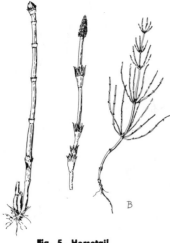

Fig. 5. Horsetail

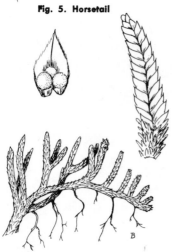

Fig. 6. Spike Moss

MOUNTAIN HOLLY FERN

(Polystichum lonchitis), Fig. 4, is a handsome evergreen fern which is found growing at high elevations in crevices of deeply shaded rocks. It is rather rare in our area. Its glossy, coarse, evergreen fronds grow from a close crown. In ours they are rarely more than 12 inches long.

HORSETAIL FAMILY

The Horsetail family is a remnant group of firm-walled, hollow-stemmed, jointed plants that have come down to us from the coal forming (antedeluvian) era of geological history. They are natives to America, Europe and Asia. The silica in their cell walls makes them a traditional scouring agent. The most common species are *Equisetum hyemale* with perennial stems of one kind (left) in Fig. 5 and *Equisetum arvense* (center and right) in Fig. 5 with two kinds of stems from a rootstock. Both species grow in moist situations and have stems about 1/4 inch thick and 1 to 3 feet high.

SELAGINELLA FAMILY

SPIKE MOSS *(Selaginella watsoni)*, Fig. 6, forms thick mats about 1 inch thick on rocky slopes and cliffs high in our mountains. It has numerous dense, prostrate branches that root along their whole length. The leaves grow in thick rows that cover the stems completely. The old leaves turn brown but remain on the stem. The new growth is vivid green. It reproduces by spores.

Trees and Shrubs

PINE FAMILY

Our first group of trees and shrubs are called gymnosperms. This is a Greek word meaning "naked seed" and refers to the seeds not being enclosed in an ovary.

WHITE FIR *(Abies concolor)*, Fig. 7, grows at moderate elevations. It is 100 to 120 feet tall, with a dense, irregular crown. Like other firs, it has single, flat, blunt, flexible needles. The cones are dark brown. The scales of fir cones drop off, leaving the central axis attached to the tree. Its wood is valuable to the building industry.

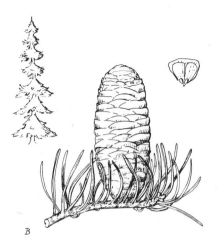

Fig. 7. White Fir

SUBALPINE FIR *(Abies lasiocarpa)*, Fig. 8, is a slender, spirelike tree which is prevalent above 8,000 feet in both the Wasatch and Uinta mountains. It rarely grows more than 80 feet tall and has little commercial value. The cones are dark purple, upright and glisten with resin.

Fig. 8. Subalpine Fir

ENGELMANN SPRUCE *(Picea engelmannii)*, Fig. 9, is a large, well-formed tree that grows at high elevations. It may be as much as 100 feet tall. Its wood, which is used extensively in the building trades, is light, soft and close grained. Spruces all have square, sharp, stiff needles. Their cones are thin and papery and hang pendulant on the branches. The cones fall in the winter after the seeds are scattered. The twigs are roughened by persistent leaf bases.

Fig. 9 Engelmann Spruce

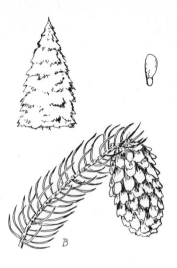

Fig. 10. Colorado Blue Spruce

Fig. 11. Lodgepole Pine

Fig. 12. Pinyon Pine

COLORADO B L U E SPRUCE (*Picea pungens*), Fig. 10, is so much like Engelmann Spruce that they are sometimes difficult to distinguish. Colorado Blue Spruce, however, is usually bluer in color, taller, less aromatic and has smoother twigs. Although it grows in both the Wasatch and Uinta mountains, it is much less common than Engelmann Spruce. It is frequently used as an ornamental.

Pines may be distinguished from other conifers by their sharp needles which are in bundles, held together by a thin sheath. Their cones are made up of thick, woody scales.

LODGEPOLE PINE (*Pinus contorta*), Fig. 11, grows in dense stands 80 to 100 feet tall at elevations up to 11,000 feet. It is a slender tree, that branches near the top. The needles are twisted and in bundles of two. Its bark is thin, scaly and orange brown to gray. The grayish cones retain their seeds for years, until opened by the heat of a forest fire. This often makes them the first trees to invade burned areas. It is the most common conifer in the Uinta mountains.

PINYON or NUT PINE (*Pinus edulis*), Fig. 12, is a low picturesque tree, 15 to 35 feet tall, with short, often crooked trunk and reddish or yellowish-brown furrowed bark. It has stiff, incurved gray-green needles, two to a bundle. It is best known for the tasty nuts which are borne in light-brown cones, 1-1/2 to 1-3/4 inches wide. It usually grows in dry gravelly soil in a belt, just above and overlapping *Juniperus osteosperma*.

LIMBER PINE *(Pinus flexilis)*, Fig. 13, is a handsome dark green, round topped tree which is frequently found growing in our mountains above 8,000 feet elevation. The bark of young trees is white or gray, but turns dark brown at maturity. Its needles, which grow five in a bundle, are stiff, stout, and curved upward. The largest limber pine ever recorded grows near the Cache County-Rich County line on Highway 89. It has been estimated to be more than 2,000 years old.

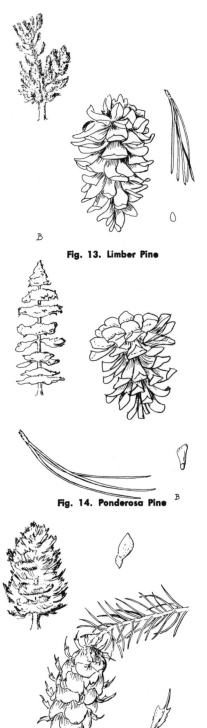

Fig. 13. Limber Pine

PONDEROSA PINE or WESTERN YELLOW PINE *(Pinus ponderosa)*, Fig. 14, is a conspicuously handsome, usually spire-like tree. It grows up to 150 feet tall and has bright yellow-green needles in bundles of three. The bark is orange-brown and scaly. The cones are reddish brown and up to 6 inches long. They shed their seed the second year. It often lives for 300 to 500 years and in a favorable environment forms nearly pure stands of open park-like forests. It is commercially valuable as wood for construction as well as interior finish.

Fig. 14. Ponderosa Pine

DOUGLAS FIR *(Pseudotsuga menziesii* var. *glauca)*, Fig. 15, is one of the most important of our western timber trees. The middle and upper branches are ascending while the lower branches droop. It has short, soft needles that have a bluish cast, especially on the new growth. Its most distinguishing characteristic, however, is the three pointed bracts on the cones.

Fig. 15. Douglas Fir

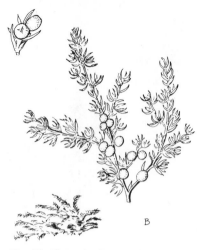

Fig. 16. Mountain Common Juniper

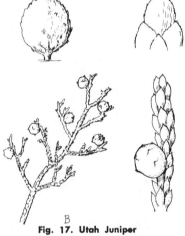

B
Fig. 17. Utah Juniper

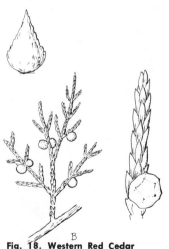

B
Fig. 18. Western Red Cedar

CYPRESS FAMILY

The Junipers have scale - like leaves and cones that resemble berries. They are common in drier locations on our mountains.

MOUNTAIN COMMON JUNIPER *(Juniperus communis)*, Fig. 16, has a dense spreading habit and is rarely more than 3 feet tall. It often covers large areas of our mountain ridges and forms dense rings under other conifers. Its awl-shaped leaves are arranged in whorles of three. The fruit is bluish and attractive.

UTAH JUNIPER *(Juniperus osteosperma)*, Fig. 17, is our most common foothill juniper. It is a dense, rounded, erect tree 8 to 15 feet tall. Its scale-like leaves are light yellowish green and its dry berries are reddish brown. It grows on dry, arid hillsides.

WESTERN RED CEDAR *(Juniperus scopulorum)*, Fig. 18, grows at higher elevations and is taller than *J. osteosperma*. It reaches 20 to 50 feet in height with either a single trunk or numerous spreading basal branches. The reddish-brown bark grows in narrow ridges and is sometimes shreddy. The dark green leaves and blue fruit are often covered with a white powdery bloom. This juniper is an important source of food for birds and browsing animals. Logan Canyon's Old Juniper is one of this species.

WILLOW FAMILY

Angiosperms are flowering plants and comprise the largest number of species in our flora. All plants that follow are members of this group.

NARROWLEAFED COTTON-WOOD *(Populus angustifolia)*, Fig. 19, is common near streams at the mouths of our canyons. It is a large spreading, fast growing, short lived tree with a sturdy trunk that may be 2 feet or more in diameter. The new bark is smooth and white, turning dark gray and rough with age. In the spring, the opening leaf buds are gummy and have a characteristic odor. The leaves are dark green and shiny. The name cottonwood refers to the cotton-like appendages on the seeds.

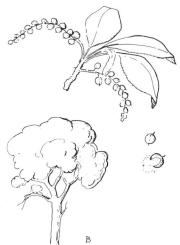

Fig. 19. Narrowleaf Cottonwood

QUAKING ASPEN *(Populus tremuloides)*, Fig. 20, is a tall slender tree with smooth white bark and delicate trembling leaves. It occurs in dense stands on moist hillsides at elevations above 6,000 feet. It grows from root sprouts and is often the first tree to grow in burned out areas, where the old roots give rise to new stands. In autumn the leaves become clear bright yellow or a golden yellow.

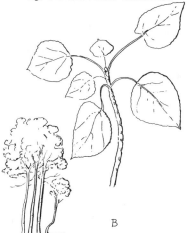

Fig. 20. Quaking Aspen

SANDBAR WILLOW *(Salix exigua)*, Fig. 21, is common on stream banks in elevations below 6,000 feet. It grows in thick stands about 6 or 8 feet tall. Its slender, flexible branches are leafy and graceful. The narrow leaves are soft and finely pubescent, giving them a silvery gray appearance. Its blossom is a loose catkin which comes in the spring along with the new leaves.

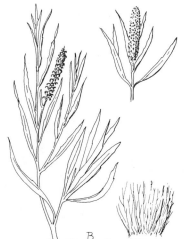

Fig. 21. Sandbar Willow

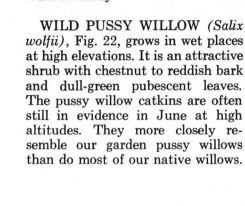

WILD PUSSY WILLOW *(Salix wolfii)*, Fig. 22, grows in wet places at high elevations. It is an attractive shrub with chestnut to reddish bark and dull-green pubescent leaves. The pussy willow catkins are often still in evidence in June at high altitudes. They more closely resemble our garden pussy willows than do most of our native willows.

Fig. 22. Wild Pussy Willow

BIRCH FAMILY

ALDER *(Alnus tenuifolia)*, Fig. 23, is a shrub or small tree which grows near streams or in other moist places. It has an attractive open habit of growth with ascending limbs and silvery-gray bark. The illustration shows left, pistillate flowers and pendulant staminate flowers; at right, the mature seed cones with their woody scales. The leaves are doubly toothed so that the primary teeth have smaller teeth on them.

Fig. 23. Alder

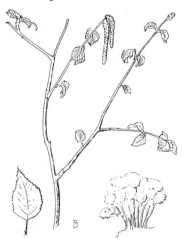

RIVER BIRCH *(Betula occidentalis)*, Fig 24, grows beside streams in clumps 30 feet high. It is distinguished by its slender unbranching habit and beautiful, hard surfaced, cherry-red bark which splits horizontally. Its leaves are delicate, rich green in summer and golden in fall. They are glandular and sticky when young. This is one of our choicest native trees.

Fig. 24. River Birch

BEECH FAMILY

GAMBEL SCRUB OAK *(Quercus gambelii)*, Fig. 25, can be found in thick stands on our foothills, usually where the soil is derived from granite rock. The rough, gnarled, gray, hardwood trunks are picturesque and ornamental. Where water is in short supply, it grows for many years without becoming taller than a shrub, but in favorable locations it will grow tall and straight. It is an important source of browse for deer, but cattle are often poisoned by eating the leaves, especially in the spring.

Fig. 25. Gambel Scrub Oak

BARBERRY FAMILY

OREGON GRAPE *(Berberis repens)*, Fig. 26, is an extremely attractive, low, woody plant that grows on semi-dry, gravelly hillsides, under shrubs and trees. In the spring it is covered with racemes of delightfully fragrant yellow flowers. The fruit is dark blue and somewhat resembles small bunches of grapes but is very acrid to the taste. Its leaves are stiff, shiny and resemble English holly in size and shape.

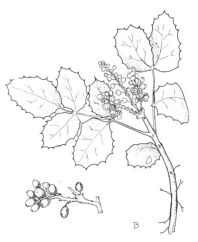

Fig. 26. Oregon Grape

SAXIFRAGE FAMILY

LITTLELEAF MOCKORANGE *(Philadelphus microphyllus)*, Fig. 27, is an erect shrub 5 feet high or less, with ex-foliating bark and ascending branches that bend downward at the ends. The blossoms, which come in June, are white, fragrant and beautiful. It closely resembles the mockorange of our gardens, except that it is smaller. It grows at high elevations in the Uinta Mountains.

Fig. 27. Littleleaf Mockorange

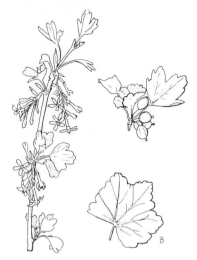

Fig. 28. Golden Currant

GOLDEN CURRANT *(Ribes aureum)*, Fig. 28, grows in round clumps on stream banks in our canyons. Its wand-like branches are about 4 feet tall. In the spring it blooms with racemes of golden flowers from the axils of the leaves. As the blossoms mature, they become rose colored. The fruit is 1/2 inch long, edible, sweet and may be any color ranging through yellow, red and black.

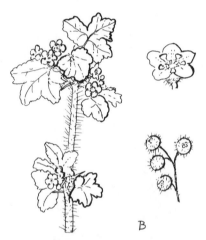

Fig. 29. Gooseberry Currant

GOOSEBERRY CURRANT *(Ribes montigenum)*, Fig. 29, is a low bristly shrub that grows on alpine slopes. The leaves are more or less deeply incised and glandular. The whole shrub is thickly armed with short sharp thorns. The yellow to pink blossoms are 3/8 inch wide and borne in short racemes. The fruit is a red, glandular, bristly berry.

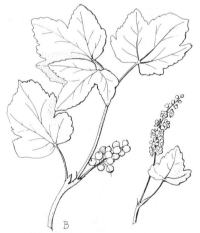

Fig. 30. Western Black Currant

WESTERN BLACK CURRANT *(Ribes peteolare)*, Fig. 30, is an erect, thornless shrub 5 to 15 feet tall that grows in shady thickets along our canyon streams. Its attractive white blossoms appear in May and June. The fruit, which matures in August, is black, ¼ inch in diameter, dull, edible and has a distinct skunky odor. This does not keep it from being a favorite fare for birds. The leaves, especially when young, are glandular and sticky. *Ribes cereum* also has no thorns, has pinkish tubular flowers and red berries. The leaves are smaller than *R. peteolare* but similar in shape. It is much branched and grows less than 4 feet high.

ROSE FAMILY

SERVICEBERRY or SARVICE-BERRY *(Amelanchier alnifolia)*, Fig. 31, is a slender shrub or small tree that grows 18 to 20 feet high in our canyons. In the spring it produces numerous short racemes of white, fragrant blossoms 1 inch wide with strap-shaped petals. The fruit matures in late summer and is dark blue or purple when ripe. It is seedy and bland, but otherwise quite palatable. Lewis and Clark discovered and used its fruit on their famous expedition. It was also once an important source of food for Indians and pioneers. It is still important to wild life. *Amelanchier utahensis* is quite similar but grows on dry hillsides and has fruit that remains dry and pulpy.

Fig. 31. Serviceberry

CURLYLEAF MAHOGANY *(Cercocarpus ledifolius)*, Fig. 32, grows in our high mountains. It is a round, brown-barked alpine tree or shrub that may be 12 feet tall. In June it has numerous pink blossoms 1/4 inch wide, that have the texture of brushed felt. The fruits are achenes, attached to feathery spiraling plumes. The thick smooth leaves are rolled back on the edges, green above and grayish beneath.

Fig. 32. Curlyleaf Mahogany

TRUE MOUNTAIN MAHOGANY *(Cercocarpus montanus)*, Fig. 33, is an alpine shrub 3 to 10 feet high that grows on dry mountain ridges. It has thin grayish-brown bark and pink blossoms 3/8 inch wide. The leaves are green above and white pubescent beneath. The fruits are almost identical to *C. ledefolius*.

Fig. 33. True Mountain Mahogany

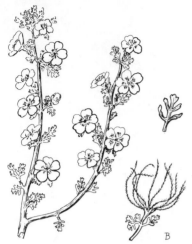

Fig. 34. Stansbury's Cliffrose

Fig. 35. Douglas Hawthorn

Fig. 36. Mountain Avens-Wood Nymph

STANSBURY'S CLIFFROSE *(Cowania mexicana* var. *stansburiana)*, Fig. 34, is an erect shrub 3 to 10 feet high with small grayish green, glandular leaves. The yellow and white blossoms come at the ends of the branches and resemble small single roses about 5/8 inch in diameter. It blooms from April to September. Its bark is gray and shreddy, but the new twigs are reddish. The inner bark has been used by some Great Basin Indians for weaving into mats, sandals, and even a cloth. It grows on dry hillsides. Stansbury's cliffrose was first collected on Stansbury Island in the Great Salt Lake.

DOUGLAS HAWTHORN *(Crateagus douglasii)*, Fig. 35, forms thickets 10 to 12 feet high along stream banks at the mouths of our canyons. It is an attractive shrub with shiny green leaves, smooth reddish-brown bark, and stems armed with stout thorns. In late April and May it is a mass of white, sweetly fragrant blossoms 3/4 inch in diameter. Its fruit is reminiscent of small, long stemmed apples that are red, becoming black at maturity. It is a favorite food of birds but is too seedy and tasteless for human consumption.

MOUNTAIN AVENS-WOOD NYMPH *(Dryas octopetala)*, Fig. 36, is one of three species of Dryas native to the Arctic and cold temperature regions of the north temperate zone. It is a low spreading shrub only a few inches high that grows in the high Uintas. The white flowers are about an inch across. The leaves are dark green above, pubescent and whitish beneath. It blooms in June and July.

BUSH ROCK SPIRAEA (*Holodiscus dumosus*), Fig. 37, is an attractive, compact shrub 3 to 12 feet tall that is branched from the base. It blooms from June to August with terminal 4 to 8 inch racemes of tiny creamy-white flowers. The leaves are quite pubescent as are the young twigs. Indians once used its small dried berries for food. It grows on hillsides and river bottoms throughout our area.

Fig. 37. Bush Rock Spiraea

TUFTED ROCKMAT (*Petrophytum caespitosum*), Fig. 38, forms a thick gnarled mat of woody stems on the face of sheer rock in our canyons and mountain sides. Its leaves are in small compact rosettes at the ends of the branches. Above this, on scapes, it bears small bottle-brush-like racemes of creamy-white blossoms. Every part of this plant is attractive, even when there is nothing remaining except the dead woody stems.

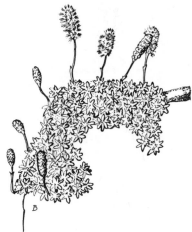

Fig. 38. Tufted Rockmat

MALLOW NINEBARK (*Physocarpus malvaceus*), Fig. 39, is one of two ninebarks in our area. Both are so called for their ex-foliating bark. This one was named "malvaceus" for the shape of the leaf, which resembles those of the mallow family. It grows 3 to 7 feet tall along our stream banks in rich, moist soil. In the spring it has short racemes of white flowers generously endowed with yellow stamens.

Fig. 39. Mallow Ninebark

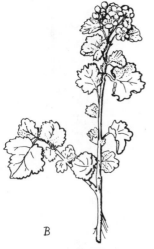

MOUNTAIN NINEBARK *(Physocarpus monogynus)*, Fig. 40, has blossoms similar to *P. malvaceus* but is a smaller shrub, usually 3 feet high in our area, and has more diffused branches. It grows on dry, rocky hillsides. *Physocarpus* is from the Greek and refers to the inflated fruit. Both bloom in June and July.

Fig. 40. Mountain Ninebark

SHRUBBY CINQUEFOIL *(Potentilla fruticosa)*, Fig. 41, grows in open rocky areas in our mountains and in such far separated places as Alaska, Labrador, Europe and Asia as well as England, California and New Mexico. Cinquefoils are one of the most abundant plants in our mountains. However, in our area *P. fruticosa* is the only member of this genus that is a shrub. Also see pages 78, 79 for other species of *Potentilla*. It grows about 3 feet tall, has gray-green leaves and yellow blossoms about 1 inch in diameter.

Fig. 41. Shrubby Cinquefoil

CHOKECHERRY *(Prunus virginiana* var. *melanocarpa)*, Fig. 42, is a shrub or small tree up to 30 feet tall, with smooth reddish-brown bark. It is found throughout our canyons. The blossoms are white with yellow stamens, and they come in racemes 2 to 4 inches long. They are very fragrant. The leaves are shiny and attractive, but are poisonous to some browsing animals in the early spring. The fruit, which individually resembles small cherries, is red, turning black at maturity. It has a pleasant, bitter astringent flavor, that is popular in jelly or a syrupy juice.

Fig. 42. Chokecherry

BITTER BRUSH *(Purshia tridentata)*, Fig. 43, derived its common name from its dry, hard intensely bitter fruit which small rodents seem to relish. It is an aromatic, much branched shrub 2 to 8 feet tall, which is often associated with sagebrush. Its numerous yellow blossoms, 1/2 inch in diameter, come at the ends of the branches in the spring. The leaves are small, fan shaped, green on top and gray beneath. Its branches are gray except when wet, when they turn red. It was named for Frederick Pursh, an early United States botanist.

Fig. 43. Bitter Brush

NOOTKA ROSE *(Rosa nutkana* var. *hispida* or *R. Spaldingii)*, Fig. 44, is the largest and most beautiful wild rose in our flora. The large solitary pale-pink blossoms, often 3 inches across, are borne on short lateral branches. They are delightfully fragrant. The leaves are slightly glandular and have a sweet resinous scent. The bush rarely grows more than 4 feet tall and is much branched. It can be found in moist, rocky soil high in our mountains.

Fig. 44. Nootka Rose

WILD R O S E *(Rosa woodsii)*, Fig. 45, is more common than the nootka rose. It grows in thick patches on road sides and side hills, forming a refuge for small wild life. It sometimes becomes 8 feet tall. The flowers commonly grow in clusters and vary in color from pale pink to deep rose. They are usually 2 inches in diameter. The seeds are achenes enclosed in hips which turn bright red in the fall.

Fig. 45. Wild Rose

Fig. 46. Wild Raspberry

Fig. 47. Western Thimbleberry

Fig. 48. Mountain Ash

WILD RASPBERRY (*Rubus idaeus* or *R. melanolasius*), Fig. 46, will be familiar to most readers because it is the parent of most of our cultivated red raspberries and closely resembles them. The 3-1/2-foot flexible branches and dark-green leaves are armed with multitudes of small thorns. The pink and white blossoms are inconspicuous behind the calyx. It blooms in June and July. The fruit, which comes in late summer, is attractive and palatable. Look for them in open wooded areas or in rock strewn slopes in our mountains.

WESTERN THIMBLEBERRY (*Rubus parviflorus*), Fig. 47, thrives at high altitudes in our mountains. It is found in large patches in canyons and open woods above 8,000 feet. It grows about 5 feet tall on slender thornless branches. The bark becomes brown and shreddy when old. Its white blossoms resemble the wild rose and are often 2 inches across. The mature leaves are about 6 inches in diameter and dark green. The fruit, when ripe, is bright red with a soft velvety texture. It is tart and palatable.

MOUNTAIN ASH (*Sorbus scopulina*), Fig. 48, has blossoms and fruit that closely resemble the cultivated European Mountain Ash. Ours, however, never grows more than 12 or 15 feet tall and is a semierect shrub that branches from the base. In the spring it is covered with large racemes made up of sweetly-fragrant white blossoms each about 1/4 inch across. The huge showy bunches of red-orange fruit mature in late summer. It is often found growing with aspen above 8,000 foot elevations.

SUMAC FAMILY

SMOOTH SUMAC *(Rhus glabra)*, Fig. 49, is common not only on our foothills but over most of the United States and southern Canada. It is an erect, few-branched shrub 6 or 7 feet tall, with leaves that turn rose and scarlet in the fall. It grows on open, dry, gravelly hillsides where vegetation is often scarce. The fruit is covered with short reddish hairs. It is a favorite with birds.

Fig. 49. Smooth Sumac

POISON IVY *(Rhus radicans)*, Fig. 50, is beautiful and treacherous. Its milky sap is highly toxic to most people. It is, nevertheless, one of the most beautiful plants we have in our canyons. In May it blooms with inconspicuous white flowers followed by waxy white berries that remain all winter. Its shiny green leaves turn brilliant red and orange in the fall. Poison ivy prefers shady, wooded, situations among small trees. It is a low shrub or sometimes a vine.

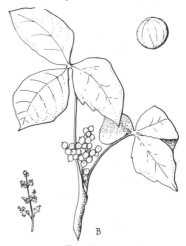

Fig. 50. Poison Ivy

SQUAW BUSH *(Rhus trilobata)*, Fig. 51, was a favorite of the Indians from the Rockies to the west coast. They used the sticky red berries for food and the flexible straight branches for basket making. This shrub rarely grows more than 4 feet tall but forms large clumps. Its yellow blossoms come before the leaves, in March or April. The leaves are soft-textured and aromatic.

Fig. 51. Squaw Bush

Fig. 52. Mountain Lover

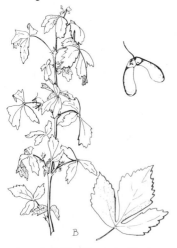

Fig. 53. Rocky Mountain Maple

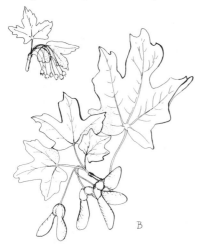

Fig. 54. Bigtooth Maple

STAFF-TREE FAMILY

MOUNTAIN LOVER *(Pachystima myrsinites)*, Fig. 52, is a low, spreading, much-branched woody shrub. It has small thick evergreen leaves reminiscent of the "boxwood" which is used in formal gardens. Unlike boxwood, however, it has a more open habit of growth and is inclined to be prostrate. You will find it on moist canyon hillsides under trees or higher shrubs. The dark-red blossoms which come in May are very small but interesting when viewed under a lens. The seed is an inconspicuous capsule.

MAPLE FAMILY

ROCKY MOUNTAIN MAPLE *(Acer glabrum)*, Fig. 53, grows at high elevations on dry rocky ridges and hillsides. It is a handsome, round, well-formed shrub with clean, smooth, gray bark. The leaves are numerous, small, glabrous; and both the simple and trifoliate varieties are in our area. It has winged seeds typical of the maple family.

BIGTOOTH MAPLE *(Acer grandidentatum)*, Fig. 54, is the most common maple in our canyons. The leaves of this tree become brilliantly colored in the autumn. It is a relatively small tree and frequently grows in pure stands, very close together. It is distinguished by the clean, smooth, gray bark, attractive leaves and even branching habit. Bigtooth maple is a hardwood and a close relative of the eastern sugar maple. It blooms in May with inconspicuous light-green flowers.

BUCKTHORN FAMILY

BOXELDER *(Acer negundo)*, Fig. 55, is the ash-leaf maple of the east coast. This prolific, short-lived softwood tree flourishes in our lower canyons and bottom lands. In open situations, it is truly magnificent, often 65 feet tall, with its straight trunk and round head. In less open places it may lean and develop an irregular form. The leaves and wood have a bitter acrid odor. The new growth is smooth and reddish brown, turning gray and rough with age.

Fig. 55. Boxelder

SNOWBUSH *(Ceanothus velutinus)*, Fig. 56, represents one of the most important and beautiful plant groups in the West. This is a low, spreading, round-topped evergreen shrub which covers large areas of our high mountain hillsides. The 3-nerved leaves are thick and leathery, varnished green above and dull tan gray beneath. The flowers are individually very small but come in conspicuous racemes that look like small drifts of snow in May and June.

Fig. 56. Snowbush

ALDER BUCKTHORN *(Rhamnus alnifolia)*, Fig. 57, is a gray barked, much branched shrub 3 to 10 feet tall that grows near streams or in bogs at high elevations. The flowers, which are small and inconspicuous, appear with the leaves in early spring. They are followed by fruit made up of three black nutlets.

Fig. 57. Alder Buckthorn

Fig. 58. Russet Buffalowberry

Fig. 59. Redosier Dogwood

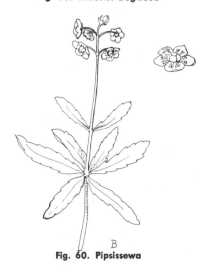

Fig. 60. Pipsissewa

OLEASTER FAMILY

RUSSET BUFFALOBERRY (*Shepherdia canadensis*), Fig. 58, is another of our high altitude shrubs. It grows 5 to 10 feet tall in the open woods where the soil remains fairly moist. While its flowers are inconspicuous, it is notable for its uniquely attractive leaves and berries. The young twigs and the under side of the leaves are silvery with rusty dots while the upper surfaces of the leaves are green and glabrous. The red and yellow berries have a transparent quality and are singularly beautiful but bitter and acrid to the taste.

REDOSIER DOGWOOD (*Cornus stolonifera*), Fig. 59, is perhaps most conspicuous for its outstanding smooth mahogany red bark. It grows in thickets, near streams throughout our canyons. In favored locations it may be 7 or 8 feet tall, though it is frequently shorter. It has flat panicles of faintly-fragrant, white blossoms in May, followed by opaque-white berries. It is one of the few of our native shrubs that has been widely introduced into our gardens.

WINTERGREEN FAMILY

PIPSISSEWA or PRINCESS PINE (*Chimaphila umbellata*), Fig. 60, is an attractive, low-growing evergreen half-shrub that can be found under conifers in the Uinta Mountains. It does not tolerate lime soil. Pipsissewa grows 4 to 8 inches tall with glossy dark-green leaves and pink or white flowers ¾ inches wide. The style, which fills the whole center of the flower, is green.

HEATH FAMILY

RED BEARBERRY *(Arctosta-phylos uva-ursi)*, Fig. 61, grows in granitic soil in the Uintas. It is a low, prostrate shrub with rooting branches and small thick, leathery leaves and whitish blossoms. Its red berries are relished by birds and many animals, including bears. Most humans find them unpalatably bitter and astringent. The Indians used the bark as an adulterant for their tobacco, and the berries for tanning hides and in various other ways. It is a primary invader, being one of the first plants to grow in burned and disturbed areas. It seems to have no elevation limitations.

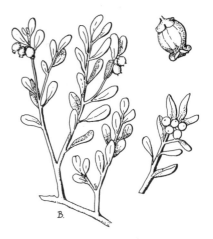

Fig. 61. Red Bearberry

BOG LAUREL *(Kalmia polifolia* var. *microphylla)*, Fig. 62, is a thoroughly delightful and beautiful plant. It can be found growing in bogs and other equally wet locations in the Uinta mountains. It is 6 to 20 inches tall, has thick leathery evergreen leaves that are rolled under on the margins. Blooming time is from June to August and it has ¾ inch pink flowers with white centers. Bog laurel is a member of the Heath family and does not tolerate lime soil.

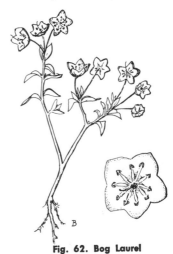

Fig. 62. Bog Laurel

LABRADOR TEA *(Ledum glandulosum)*, Fig. 63, is a stout, erect, rigidly branched shrub that grows 1 to 5 feet tall. Its leaves are leathery, fragrant and resinous, dark green above and gray beneath. The showy white flowers come in 2 inch clusters at the ends of the branches in May and June. Look for it at altitudes up to 12,000 feet in the Uinta mountains and in canyons east of Salt Lake Valley.

Fig. 63. Labrador Tea

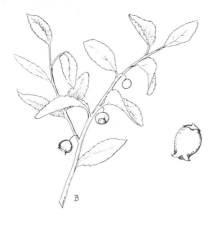

Fig. 64. Blue Huckleberry

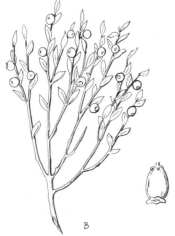

Fig. 65. Grouse Whortleberry

rig. 66. Spreading Dogbane

BLUE HUCKLEBERRY or BLUEBERRY *(Vaccinium membranaceum)*, Fig. 64, grows in the Uinta and Wasatch Mountains in soils derived from granite and quartzite rocks. It is usually about 4 feet tall and has thin deciduous leaves that are green above and paler beneath. It blooms in June and July with rather inconspicuous yellow blossoms. The fruit, which ripens in late summer, is about ¼ to ⅓ inch in diameter, dark red or purplish blue, attractive, aromatic and delicious.

GROUSE WHORTLEBERRY *(Vaccinium scoparium)*, Fig. 65, is found in the Uinta Mountains. It is a low, finely-branched shrub that grows to about 15 inches tall. The bark has small vertical ridges or wings which are an identifying characteristic. The leaves are pale green and shining above and dull beneath. The flowers come in July and are pink and inconspicuous. They are followed in late summer with light-red fruit that is very palatable and much sought after by people, wild animals, and birds.

DOGBANE FAMILY

SPREADING DOGBANE *(Apocynum androsaemifolium)*, Fig. 66, branches from near the ground with slender, smooth branches and drooping leaves. The whole plant seldom is more than 18 inches tall. It grows on hillsides and open woods in our canyons. It blooms in June and July with pink flowers from the axils of the leaves. They are less than ½ inch long. It has long, woody, double seed pods that split down one side to let out seeds with hairy appendages.

COMMON DOGBANE *(Apocynum cannabinum)*, Fig. 67, is very similar to *A. androsaemifolium.* However, it has a more erect habit of growth and is a little taller, growing from 3 to 4 feet. The leaves are ascending rather than drooping and the pink blossoms are shorter and wider. It grows on ditch banks and semi-shady places. The ancient Greeks mistakenly thought *Apocynum* to be poisonous to dogs. It *is* poisonous to livestock. The stems contain a tough fiber that was used by the Indians for cordage.

Fig. 67. Common Dogbane

PHLOX FAMILY

PRICKLY GILIA *(Leptodactylon watsonii)*, Fig. 68, grows only a few inches high but spreads to a width of 12 to 14 inches. Its sharp, needle-like leaves are opposite and almost ½ inch long. The old leaves remain on the plant while new growth comes at the branch tips. The flowers are satin-textured, white or pinkish and have considerable variation in size. They bloom in April and May. It grows on cliffs and rocky hills. It is frequently confused with *L. pungems* which has very similar flowers but grows on rocky ridges and has shorter, close set leaves on slender branches 4 to 32 inches long. The old leaves do not remain on the plant.

Fig. 68. Prickly Gilia

HONEYSUCKLE FAMILY

TWIN BERRY *(Lonicera involucrata)*, Fig. 69, is well named for the double, shiny-black fruit, encircled by rose-colored involucral bracts. They are beautiful but have a disagreeable flavor. The flowers that come in June and July are yellow. It is an attractive woody shrub found in moist, rocky places high in our mountains.

Fig. 69. Twin Berry

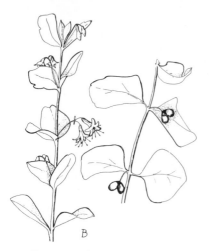

Fig. 70. Utah Honeysuckle

UTAH HONEYSUCKLE *(Lonicera utahensis)*, Fig. 70, blooms in late spring and early summer with white or yellow trumpet-shaped flowers in pairs. The berries are slightly united, bright red and unpalatable. These shrubs are associated with pine forests high in our mountains. They are rarely more than 5 feet tall.

Fig. 71. Blueberry Elder

BLUEBERRY ELDER *(Sambucus caerulea)*, Fig. 71, is very common in our canyons. It has straight, jointed, hollow stems that grow in thick clumps 10 to 12 feet high. White lacy flowers are arranged in panicles. In late summer, they bear large bunches of dark-blue fruit which is often whitened with powdery bloom. The berries are sour when eaten raw, but make excellent jelly, syrup, etc. Almost every part of this shrub was used by the Indians for everything from musical instruments to food.

Fig. 72. Snowberry

SNOWBERRY *(Symphoricarpos oreophilus* var. *utahensis)*, Fig. 72, is familiar in our gardens as well as our mountains. In its native environment, it grows on wooded hill sides, often associated with aspen. It is an erect, much branched shrub with opposite leaves, small pink flowers, and white porcelain-like berries. It is a valuable food source for birds and small mammals but is unpalatable for human consumption. The Indians made a medical concoction from the roots.

SUNFLOWER FAMILY

SAGEBRUSH *(Artemisia)*, is perhaps the most widely known plant in the Intermountain Region. Not only is it common to our dry foothills and plains, but it played a large part in the lives of native Indians and our early pioneers. It was used extensively for fuel, medication for digestive disorders, a yellow dye, and as a beauty treatment for hair. Indians used its smoke to neutralize odors left from an encounter with a skunk. There are over 100 species. DWARF SAGEBRUSH *(Artemisia nova)*, Fig. 73, is a low, spreading, evergreen shrub 4 to 16 inches tall that can be found on dry, rocky and gravelly mountainsides in the Wasatch and Uinta mountains. The old bark is brown and shreddy while the twigs are striated green and brown. The leaves are almost glabrous, green or gray green and aromatic. It blooms from August to October.

Fig. 73. Dwarf Sagebrush

HOARY SAGEBRUSH *(Artemisia cana)*. Fig. 74, is a low, round shrub 1 to 3½ feet high with close, erect branches and silvery-white, mildly-aromatic leaves. It blooms with small yellow flowers in August and September. It is tolerant to alkali soil.

Fig. 74. Hoary Sagebrush

BIG SAGEBRUSH *(Artemisia tridentata)*, Fig. 75, is 1 to 10 feet high with a stout trunk and a few ascending branches. The mature bark is gray and shreddy. It is rounded or somewhat flattened on top. The evergreen leaves are gray green to yellowish white and very aromatic. It grows on foothills and mountain sides in non-saline, rocky soil. Its blossoms are yellow and very small. It blooms in late summer.

Fig. 75. Big Sagebrush

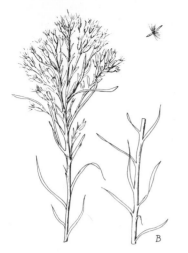

Fig. 76. Rabbitbrush

RABBITBRUSH *(Chrysothamnus nauseosus)*, Fig. 76, is a thick, woody, low-branching shrub 2 to 5 feet tall that is often associated with sagebrush on our dry foothills. It blooms in late summer with thick clusters of yellow blossoms that are followed only days later with mature seed. Its leaves are heavily aromatic, pubescent and gray green. It is named rabbitbrush because those animals find it a favorite shelter. The Indians used it in making yellow dye. It has been found to contain varying amounts of high grade rubber but not enough to be commercially profitable. Sticky rabbitbrush *(C. viscidiflorus)* is similar but not so tall.

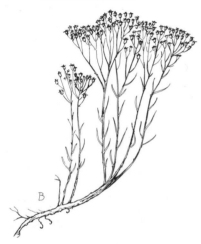

Fig. 77. Broom Snakeweed

BROOM SNAKEWEED *(Gutierrezia sarothrae)*, Fig. 77, is a subshrub with s p r e a d i n g twiggy branches 12 to 24 inches high. The yellow flowers are borne in flat-topped panicles and bloom May to October. They grow on dry hillsides.

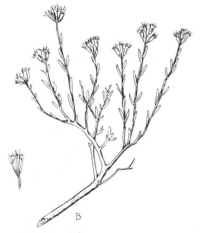

Fig. 78. Spineless Gray Horsebrush

SPINELESS GRAY HORSE-BRUSH *(Tetradymia canescens)*, Fig. 78, is a much-branched shrub 8 to 24 inches high that grows on our foothills. It has white hairs on the stem and leaves. The yellow blossoms come in groups of four at the ends of branches. It also has only four bracts. *Tetradymia* means four and together, so it is well named. It blooms from June to September.

Climbing and Twining Plants

CROWFOOT FAMILY

While climbing plants are quite prevalent in our canyons, there are not many different genera represented in our area. BLUE CLEMATIS *(Clematis columbiana)*, Fig. 79, is one of the most attractive. It is a half-woody climber with slender stems that grows at high elevations in our mountains. It blooms from May to August. The sepals are petal-like, pale lavender blue, nearly 2 inches long, and have a thin, transparent quality. The center of the flower is made up of numerous yellow and white stamens and pistils.

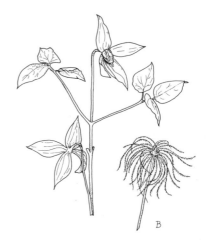

Fig. 79. Blue Clematis

WESTERN VIRGIN BOWER *(Clematis ligusticifolia)*, Fig. 80, is common at lower elevations in our canyons. It has rope-like woody stems with exfoliating bark that climb over bushes and trees. In early spring it has 3 inch clusters of white blossoms followed in late summer by plumy fruits.

Fig. 80. Western Virgin Bower

MULBERRY FAMILY

AMERICAN HOPS *(Humulus americanus)*, Fig. 81, has rough stems that are generously armed with small curved prickles. It grows in moist places in our canyons and climbs on bushes. The flowers are of two kinds: The staminite blossoms that come in clusters and produce prodigious amounts of yellow pollen, and the pistillate flowers that come in pairs and are made up of leafy, imbricated bracts, generously sprinkled with yellow, aromatic resinous grains. They bloom in July and August.

Fig. 81. American Hops

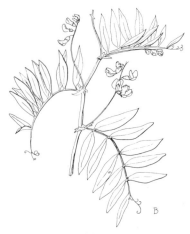

Fig. 82. Wild Sweet Pea

Fig. 83. Wild Sweet Pea

Fig. 84. American Vetch

PEA FAMILY

Wild sweet peas are rather rare in our area and rarely come in large mass plantings. Watch for them in protected wooded areas where they climb on u n d e r b r u s h. WILD SWEET PEA *(Lathyrus lanszwertii)*, Fig. 82, is a semi-climbing perennial about 2 feet high. It blooms in May and June with white blossoms, sometimes tinged with purple. It can be found along canyon streams and on moist hillsides. The seed pods are a little over an inch long and glabrous. *Lathyrus leucanthus* is similar and can be found growing in open woods and near streams between 8,000 and 11,000 feet elevation. Its blossoms are entirely white.

WILD SWEET PEA *(Lathyrus pauciflorus)*, Fig. 83, is the largest and showiest of our wild peas. It grows 3 feet or more high and in May has numerous racemes of flowers, each with three to seven blossoms, an inch long. They are delicate lavender pink when they first bloom but turn greenish blue with age. It grows in moist soil in open woods or near streams and frequently grows in stands of Gamble oak.

AMERICAN VETCH *(Vicia americana)*, Fig. 84, is a slender, trailing or climbing plant 2 to 3 feet high. It grows on talus slopes, in open pine woods, and elevations between 5,000 and 10,000 feet. The flowers are rose purple and showy. The leaves and stems are almost glabrous. Some tribes of Indians used the young shoots of this plant for food.

Herbaceous Flowering Plants

MONOCOTYLEDONS

CATTAIL FAMILY

The cattail family is represented here by two species whose 6 or 8 foot, brown fruiting stalks and grass-like leaves are familiar in marshy places in late summer and fall. They are both known as *Cattails* and can be distinguished from each other mainly by the difference in their habits of flowering. In *Typha latifolia*, left in Fig. 85, the inflorescence is continuous on the stem. *Typha domingensis*, center in Fig. 85, has a space of naked stem between its pistillate and steminate flowers. To the right is a mature fruiting stalk with the small fuzzy seeds breaking away.

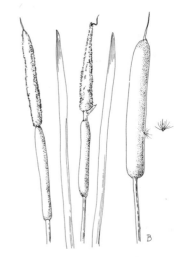

Fig. 85. Cattail

PONDWEED FAMILY

SAGO PONDWEED *(Potamogeton pectinatus)*, Fig. 86, grows submersed in water on the bottom of ponds or very slow moving streams. Its seeds are often very n u m e r o u s. Sago pondweed is thought to be the most important plant food for water birds.

Fig. 86. Sago Pondweed

WATER PLANTAIN FAMILY

ARROWHEAD *(Sagittaria cuneata)*, Fig. 87, is an attractive aquatic which may be found growing in water in the edges of mountain ponds and marshes. Its leaves are smooth, thick, and shiny. The flowers are borne in whorls on smooth stems and are white with yellow stamens. Tubers, produced on some species, served as a valuable food source for some tribes of Indians.

Fig. 87. Arrowhead

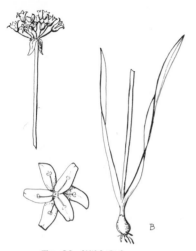

Fig. 88. Wild Onion

Fig. 89. Brandegee Onion

Fi.g 90. Wild Hyacinth

LILY FAMILY

WILD ONION *(Allium acuminatum)*, Fig. 88, forms bright pink carpets of bloom on sagebrush hillsides and along roadways in May and June. It grows 6 to 8 inches tall in dry, gravelly soil and disappears soon after blooming time. It is easily identifed by the onion odor of its flowers, leaves and edible bulbous roots. Care should be taken not to confuse it with the bulbs of D E A T H C A M A S *(Zigadenus)* which are deadly poisonous.

BRANDEGEE ONION *(Allium brandegei)*, Fig. 89, grows at middle elevations while the soil is still moist. Its blossoms, which are exceeded by narrow leaves, are more open and paler than *A. acuminatum*. It may be pink or almost white. The bulb is edible and onion flavored.

WILD HYACINTH *(Brodiaea douglasii)*, Fig. 90, grows in drying fields and hillsides, often in association with Gambel oak. Its lilac blue flowers are about an inch across, thick petaled and have a frosted appearance. They are borne at the top of a slender, perfectly round, smooth scape that may be 1 to 3 feet high and is so weak that the slightest breeze is likely to capsize it under the weight of its heavy blossom head unless it has the support of other plants. Its fragrance is delicate and delightful. Look for it about the end of May on our foothills and lower canyons. In 1828 David Douglas, a western plant explorer and botanist, sent *Brodiaea* bulbs to England where it is still a favorite in their gardens. The plants arise from bulbs.

SEGO LILY *(Calochortus nuttallii)*, Fig. 91, is Utah's state flower and one of the loveliest of our native plants. Plants often become a foot high and are topped with flowers nearly 3 inches across. Its satiny-white petals are marked at their base with velvety patches of dark maroon and yellow. The stems arise from a bland tasting bulb which the western Indians and Mormon Pioneers used for food. The name "Sego lily" is of Indian origin and unique to Utah. In California it is called Mariposa lily, which in Spanish means butterfly.

Fig. 91. Sego Lily

BLUE CAMAS LILY *(Camassia quamash)* Fig. 92, grows in moist places throughout our area. They bloom in May, often covering meadows with color that resembles clear blue water. The flowers, which are 1½ inches across, are borne on stiff, smooth stems more than a foot high. Their bulbs served as an important source of food for several Indian tribes. Disputes with white settlers over camas fields caused one of the bloodiest Indian uprisings in the northwest. Kamas, Utah, was named for this plant.

Fig. 92. Blue Camas Lily

FAIRY BELLS *(Disporum trachycarpum)*, Fig. 93, is a shade loving, branching herbaceous plant that grows on moist, wooded slopes. It grows 1 to 1½ feet tall and in early May blooms with pairs of white, bell-shaped flowers ¾ inch long. In August the fruit is scarlet and has the texture of red velvet. It occurs sparsely throughout the Wasatch and Uinta Mountains.

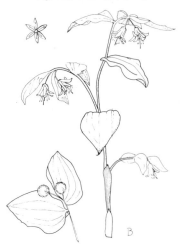

Fig. 93. Fairy Bells

Fig. 94. Dog-Tooth Violet

DOG-TOOTH VIOLET *(Erythronium grandiflorum)*, Fig 94, blooms on sparsely wooded mountain hillsides only a few feet from the receding snow. The stems arise from a deepset perennial corm. It produces two basal leaves and a 2 to 10 inch scape with one to several delicate, fragrant, yellow blossoms. In favored locations, they often become so abundant that they cover an entire hillside with sheets of color. Closely related *Erythroniums* may be found in mountains from California to Maine.

Fig. 95. Leopard Fritillaria

LEOPARD FRITILLARIA *(Fritillaria atropurpurea)*, Fig. 95, has almost perfect camouflage protection. Its mottled petals of rusty brown and pale green are all but indistinguishable in the wooded areas where they grow. Its blossoms are about an inch across and come at the top of smooth wirey stems about 10 inches tall. The blossoms are nodding on the stem, but the seed pod is erect. They bloom in May.

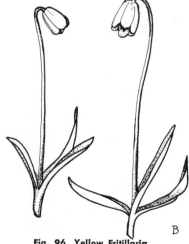

Fig. 96. Yellow Fritillaria

YELLOW FRITILLARIA *(Fritillaria pudica)*, Fig. 96, blooms in April on drying hillsides and at the mouths of canyons. The fresh yellow blossom is borne at the top of a crisp fiberless scape about 6 inches high. As the blossom matures, the petals develop a tinge of red. As in all Fritillarias, the stems arise from a white corm. This flower is becoming rare as civilization encroaches upon its natural habitat.

FALSE SOLOMON SEAL
(*Smilacina racemosa*), Fig. 97, is a
shade and moisture-loving plant
about 24 inches high that grows
under trees in our canyons. It
blooms in April with terminal
racemes of creamy or white blossoms that are small and close set.
The berries are red or red with
purple dots and have a transparent
quality.

Fig. 97. False Solomon Seal

STARRY SOLOMON SEAL
(*Smilacina stellata*), Fig. 98, is
distinguished from *Smilacina racemosa* by its star-shaped, white
flowers, narrow smooth leaves and
striped fruit. They both bloom in
April and prefer rich, moist soil.
The fruit, which matures in July,
is pale green, marked with blackish
red stripes. Both species have large
creeping rootstocks and grow in
thick stands.

Fig. 98. Starry Solomon Seal

FALSE HELLEBORE (*Vera-
trum californicum*), Fig. 99, is a
coarse, conspicuous plant which
grows in moist places. It has a
single branching panicle of flowers
3 to 6 feet tall. The individual
blossoms are ¾ inch across and are
green and white. The large yellow
green leaves as well as the flowers
attract attention. The roots and
young shoots of these plants are
poisonous to livestock and cause
deformity in unborn lambs.

Fig. 99. False Hellebore

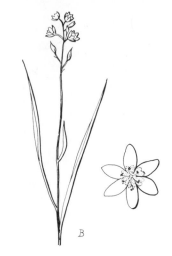

Fig. 100. Mountain Deathcamas

MOUNTAIN DEATHCAMAS (*Zigadenus elegans*), Fig. 100, is a slender, unbranched, erect plant 24 to 30 inches tall, that grows in moist places in our high mountains. It blooms in July and August with racemes of white blossoms ½ inch long that are marked at the base with small green glands. The stamens have black anthers. The stems arise from a coated bulb. The whole plant is poisonous if eaten, but generally less so than *Z. paniculatus*.

Fig. 101. Foothill Deathcamas

FOOTHILL DEATHCAMAS (*Zigadenus paniculatus*), Fig. 101, is showy on our foothills in May. Its erect, stiff stems that often reach 18 inches in height, are flanked with smooth grass-like basal leaves arranged in formal balance on three sides. The creamy white blossoms have orange stamens that give them a soft, lacy quality. It is very poisonous to livestock and people.

Fig. 102. Rocky Mountain Iris

ROCKY MOUNTAIN IRIS (*Iris missouriensis*), Fig. 102, may grow 3 feet high but is usually shorter. It reproduces from its rhizomes and seeds and forms solid masses of plants that bloom from May to September. The flowers are whitish to blue with darker venation and a yellow stripe on the falls. The blossoms are generally taller than the leaves. In our area it can be found in the Uinta Mountains and on the east side of the Wasatch Mountains.

BLUE-EYED GRASS *(Sisyrinchium angustifolium)*, Fig. 103, is another of our native meadow plants. Both the stems and leaves are flat and grass-like. Fresh flowers of one day's duration arise on slender stems from an enclosing sheath at the apex of the stem. Its flowers are violet blue with a yellow center and 1 inch in diameter. The underside of the petals are paler than the top. It blooms in late spring and early summer and frequently grows in saline soil.

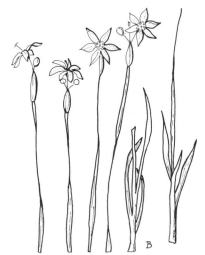

Fig. 103. Blue-eyed Grass

ORCHID FAMILY

YELLOW LADIES SLIPPER *(Cypripedium parviflorum)*, Fig. 104, was once quite common in the rich soil of our canyons and river bottoms, but is now nearly extinct. It still grows in the eastern United States. Its fragrant yellow blossoms with their reddish-brown spots are borne on 1 to 2 foot stems. Sometimes the blossoms remain 3 weeks before fading. It is one of our choicest wild flowers, but so rare that most of us will not find it in a lifetime of looking. BROWNIE LADYSLIPPER *(C. fasciculatum)* is similar in shape to *C. paviflorum*, but is much smaller and has woolly pubescent stems. It grows in the Lake Blanche area, in moist woods.

Fig. 104. Yellow Ladies Slipper

BOG ORCHID *(Habenaria dilatata)*, Fig. 105, has delightfully fragrant waxy-white blossoms on a thick hollow spike 1 to 3 feet tall. The flowers are usually less than ½ inch across. They can be found blooming in high mountain meadows in mid-summer. The leaves are smooth, green and attractive.

Fig. 105. Bog Orchid

Fig. 106. Ladies Tresses

Fig. 107. Stinging Nettle

Fig. 108. Matted Eriogonum

LADIES TRESSES *(Spiranthes romanzoffiana)*, Fig. 106, might be mistaken for bog orchid *(H. dilatata)* but the leaves are basal and the flowers are not spurred. The blossoms on ladies tresses form a s p i r a l pattern that resembles plaited-hair and accounts for the common name. Its spikes a r e shorter than those of the bog orchid.

DICOTYLEDONS

NETTLE FAMILY

STINGING NETTLE *(Urtica dioica)*, Fig. 107, is not a showy plant but is armed with stinging hairs on the leaves and stems. Contact with the skin brings one to immediate and painful awareness. Nettle grows in damp places, usually along streams. It reaches about 4 feet in height and has numerous, small, greenish-white blossoms in summer.

BUCKWHEAT FAMILY

Members of the buckwheat family make up an important part of the flora on dry hillsides and rock ledges in our mountains. They are characterized by straight stems, swollen and sheathed joints and flowers made up of six petal-like sepals. MATTED ERIOGONUM *(Eriogonum caespitosum)*, Fig. 108, has erect blossoms stalks 3 to 6 inches high and grows in clumps 8 to 12 inches in diameter. The leaves are woolly pubescent and gray. The flowers are yellow, touched with rose. They bloom May to August on our canyon hillsides.

SLENDERBUSH BUCK-WHEAT *(Eriogonum microthecum)*, Fig. 109, may be found at high altitudes in the mountains. It has a woody, much-branched stem with exfoliating bark. It grows 4 to 12 inches tall, and has terminal umbels of small white flowers with pink stripes. It blooms from June to October.

Fig. 109. Slenderbush Buckwheat

SULPHUR FLOWERED BUCK-WHEAT *(Eriogonum umbellatum)*, Fig. 110, grows about 12 to 14 inches tall and has blossoms that are bright, sulphur yellow at the top of sturdy stems. Its leaves are glabrate, green above and pubescent beneath. *Eriogonum heracleoides* is similar except for the color of the blossoms that are cream colored and the leaves that are gray green, pubescent and have a rag-like texture.

Fig. 110. Sulfur Flowered Buckwheat

WATER LADYSTHUMB *(Polygonum amphibium)*, Fig. 111, can be found floating or submersed in our mountain lakes. It has lustrous dark-green leaves and 1 to 1½ inch spikes of pink flowers that project above the surface of the water. It blooms in July and August. The stems that arise from elongated, perennial rootstocks are 20 to 40 inches long. In places where the water recedes they adapt as land plants by sprouting erect stems and roots at the nodes. *Polygonum coccineum* is a similar water plant but has more pointed leaves, and longer, narrow, pale-pink blossom spikes. They both reproduce by seed as well as rootstocks.

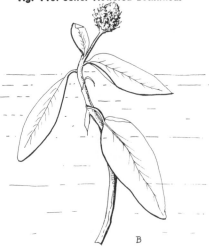

Fig. 111. Water Ladysthumb

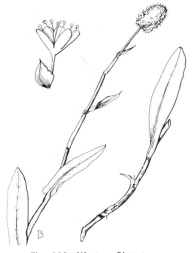

Fig. 112. Western Bistort

WESTERN BISTORT *(Polygonum bistortoides)*, Fig. 112, grows in rich damp situations, frequently associated with blue camas lily. Its leaves are smooth and green, but the sheaths and stems are often touched with rose. The blossom is a terminal raceme, white or pale rose colored, with a sweet nauseating odor. It grows about 18 inches high and blooms in mid-May. Below the leaves it has wrinkled sheathes, completely surrounding the stem.

Fig. 113. Spotted Ladysthumb

SPOTTED LADYSTHUMB *(Polygonum persicaria)*, Fig. 113, was introduced from Europe and is now found across the continent. It is a branching annual 8 to 20 inches high with numerous, pinkish, cup-shaped blossoms in racemes from May to October. The stamens are white. The leaves are smooth, green and slightly variegated. The racemes are about 1 inch long. It grows in moderately moist soil in sunny locations.

Fig. 114. Curly Dock

CURLY DOCK — INDIAN TOBACCO *(Rumex crispus)*, Fig. 114, is a common perennial in moist places in our canyons and on roadsides. The wavy margins on its leaves distinguish it from other species of *Rumex*. It blooms in May with bright yellowish green, loosely whorled racemes. At maturity it is 3 or 4 feet tall. The fruit, which matures in late summer and fall, is dark rusty brown. It remains all winter and is frequently collected for winter bouquets. It was introduced from Europe.

WILD RHUBARB or WILD BEGONIA *(Rumex venosus)*, Fig. 115, is an erect perennial 12 to 24 inches high that grows in sandy soil. It can be found along the Wasatch front. *Rumex hymeno-sepalus* is similar but has smaller seeds. It was called Wild Rubarb by early settlers who used it for food. The Navaho Indians used the fleshy, tuberous roots for making a yellow dye for their wool and in tanning hides.

Fig. 115. Wild Begonia

FOUR O'CLOCK FAMILY

SNOWBALL SAND-VERBENA *(Abronia fragrans)*, Fig. 116, prefers dry, sandy situations. The whole plant is about 18 inches high and loosely branched. The individual blossoms are ⅜ inches wide, fragrant, white and funnel-shaped with yellow deep inside the throat. The stems and leaves are yellowish gray green and very pubescent. It grows on our foothills.

Fig. 116. Snowball Sand-Verbena

PURSLANE FAMILY

WESTERN SPRING BEAUTY *(Claytonia lanceolata)*, Fig. 117, is one of the earliest and most beautiful of our spring flowers. It grows at lower and middle elevations in all our canyons and prefers rich moist soil in semi-shady locations. It rises from a deep-seated corm and usually produces two succulent green leaves close to the ground. The blossoms come from late April to July, depending upon the elevation. The stem is succulent, 2 to 6 inches high, usually unbranched and has umbels or recemes of pink or pink and white striped flowers with two sepals. The flowers are about ½ inch across.

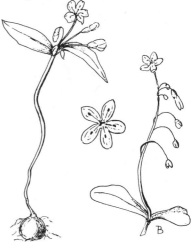

Fig. 117. Western Spring Beauty

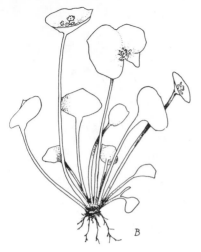

Fig. 118. Miner's Lettuce

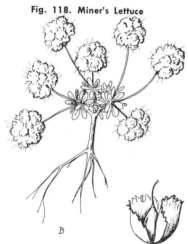

Fig. 119. Pussy Paw

Fig. 120. King's Sandwort

MINER'S LETTUCE *(Montia perfoliata)*, Fig. 118, received its common name because its mild crisp leaves and stems were eaten by early settlers and prospectors. It is a low-growing, unbranching plant, rarely more than 10 inches high. The small, white or pinkish flowers are encircled by leaves united to form a dish. They can be found growing in most of our canyons in moist, shady places. It blooms from February to April. Its blooms from February to April.

PUSSY PAW *(Spraguea umbellata)*, Fig. 119, is a low, spreading alpine plant with dense pink and white flowers at the apex of a 5 inch stem. The blossoms are short-lived but are followed immediately by cream-colored fruits that closely resemble a blossom. The rosette of fleshy basal leaves are green touched with rose. They grow in sand and fine gravel at high elevations in the Uinta Mountains.

PINK FAMILY

The members of the pink family were so named because some of them have petals whose margins are "pinked." They also have smooth stems with swollen joints and leaves that are entire and opposite. KING'S SANDWORT *(Arenaria kingii)*, Fig. 120, is a low, thick, tufted plant found on dry, rocky hillsides. The leaves are needle-like, and dark green. The blossoms are waxy white with green centers and yellow stamens. STARRY CHICKWEED *(Cerastium beeringianum)* grows at high elevations and is found in the Uinta Mountains. It may be confused with *A. kingii*. It is about the same height (8 inches) but has shorter, broader leaves and notched petals.

COW SOAPWORT *(Saponaria vaccaria)*, Fig. 121, has clear-pink blossoms about ⅝ inch across. The stems, calyx and leaves are glabrous, smooth and gray green. It grows 2 to 3 feet high on dry, gravelly hillsides in our lower canyons. The fruit is inflated and five parted. This native of Europe is rapidly becoming naturalized in the United States. It blooms in July and August.

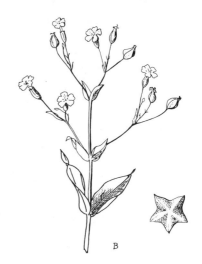

Fig. 121. Cow Soapwort

MOSS CAMPION *(Silene acaulis)*, Fig. 122, is the special reward of those who climb to the mountain tops. It is a low, densely matted, cushion-like perennial usually less than 2 inches tall that inhabits areas in rock crevices and high exposed ridges in alpine areas of North America, Canada, Europe and Asia. The stems are woody and densely covered with short needle-like leaves. The new growth comes at the ends of the branches while the old leaves remain dried on the stems. They bloom from July to August with multitudes of small pink blossoms, each ⅜ inch across.

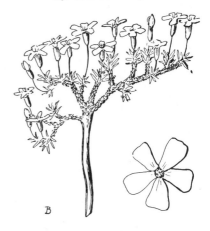

Fig. 122. Moss Campoin

DOUGLAS SILENE *(Silene douglasii)*, Fig. 123, has gray green, finely pubescent leaves and stems. The flowers are about ¾ inch across and white with green stamens. It grows 8 to 24 inches tall on dry hillsides at lower elevations and blooms in June and July. PETERSON SILENE *(Silene petersoni)*, is similar to Douglas silene but smaller. It grows in loose, chalky soil at high elevations. This was named for the late Dr. Elmer G. Peterson, former president of Utah State University.

Fig. 123. Douglas' Silene

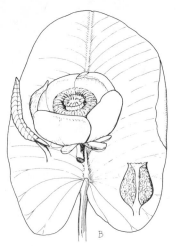

Fig. 124. Yellow Pond Lily

WATER LILY FAMILY

YELLOW POND LILY *(Nuphar polysepalum)*, Fig. 124, grows in high mountain lakes and ponds. The thick leaves float on the surface of the water. The tubers are anchored in rich mud at the bottom. The 3 inch yellow flowers are held upright, above the leaves, by slender stems. They are not fragrant as are most water lilies but are hardier. This is the only pond lily native to our area.

Fig. 125. Monkshood

BUTTERCUP FAMILY

Many of our most beautiful wild flowers are members of the buttercup family. They include regular and irregular flowers and some that have hoods and spurs. MONKSHOOD *(Aconitum columbianum)*, Fig. 125, is a handsome, erect, branching perennial 30 inches tall. It grows in damp, shady places in our high mountains. Look for it in aspen groves. In July and August it blooms with interesting royal blue flowers almost an inch wide that have pom-poms of yellow stamens. The sheltering "hood" at the top of the blossom gave it its name. It is somewhat poisonous but less so than delphiniums.

Fig. 126. Baneberry

BANEBERRY *(Actaea rubra* subsp. *arguta)*, Fig. 126, blooms in cool, wet places in our canyons. It grows 4 feet tall with terminal racemes of frothy white blossoms. The many seeded berries, that mature in July, are of two colors. They are either clear bright red or porcelain white with a black spot opposite the stem. The white berries are somewhat the larger of the two. Both are mildly poisonous if eaten.

WINDFLOWER — PACIFIC ANEMONE *(Anemone multifida)*, Fig. 127, is a hillside, alpine plant that grows at elevations of 8,000 to 12,000 feet. It grows up to 18 inches tall from a sturdy rootstock. The plants are erect and branching with pubescent stems and leaves. The blossoms are about an inch in diameter and somewhat variegated in color. They freqeuntly have shades of purple, red or yellow all in the same flower. The name *Anemone* comes from the Greek and means "flower shaken by the wind." What appears to be petals are really sepals. The petals are missing in all species of *Anemone*.

Fig. 127. Windflower

Fig. 128. Western Wood Anemone

WESTERN WOOD ANEMONE *(Anemone quinquefolia)*, Fig. 128, has a delicate white blossom an inch wide on a slender stalk which grows 6 to 12 inches tall. The leaves are thin, soft and vivid-green. They are not common in our area but can be found blooming in May and June in some moist shady places. They are often associated with alpine fir and Engelmann spruce.

ANEMONE *(Anemone zephyra)*, Fig. 129, is one of the most beautiful of the anemones. It has sturdy, erect stems 20 inches tall, mostly with solitary flowers on each stem. The flowers are 2 inches in diameter and white or in shades of clear yellow. It grows in rich, moist soil at high elevations, mostly above 10,000 feet. In our area, it can be found in the Uinta Mountains.

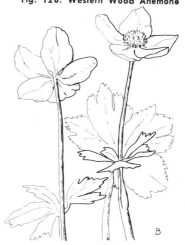

Fig. 129. Anemone

Fig. 130. Colorado Columbine

Fig. 131. Northwestern Crimson Columbine

Fig. 132. Marshmarigold

Columbines are quite common in limited areas of our mountains. The spurs have been likened to doves crowding around a small dish. Hence the common name columbine — a dove. COLORADO COLUMBINE *(Aquilegia caerulea)*, Fig. 130, grows on cool, moist hillsides at high altitudes in both the Wasatch and Uinta Mountains. It has thin green leaves that are mostly basal. The blossoms are borne on slender, smooth green stems about 2 feet tall. It blooms in July and August with flowers which may be as much as 4 inches across, and have spurs 1 to 2 inches long. The petals vary in color from cream to white and the petal-like sepals from white to deep blue. Both are delicate and tissue thin. This is Colorado's state flower.

NORTHWEST CRIMSON COLUMBINE *(Aquilegia formosa)*, Fig. 131, is a round, much branched plant with compact blossoms 2 inches across. The spurs and sepals are red and the petals yellow. It grows throughout our area in moist open woods and near streams. It is frequently associated with CALIFORNIA COLUMBINE *(A. flavescens)* which is very similar except that the flowers are entirely yellow.

MARSHMARIGOLD *(Caltha leptosepala)*, Fig. 132, is a succulent perennial that grows in rich, wet soil, frequently near stands of lodgepole pine. It forms a thick crown above fleshy roots. The leaves are glabrous and basal. Plants usually produce two flowers with attractive white blossoms on 12 inch scapes. It has no petals, only sepals. It blooms in June and July.

Delphinium is a Greek word meaning dolphin flower (from the shape of the bud). LOW LARK-SPUR *(Delphinium nelsoni)*, Fig. 133, is the showy lavender-blue delphinium that is common on our foothills in May. It reaches about 12 inches in height and is generally unbranched. Its root is tuber-like and along with its leaves, is quite poisonous to cattle but not to sheep. On dry foothills it grows quickly in early spring and produces its flowering stalk while the winter moisture is still in the ground. It then produces seed and dries off for another year.

Fig. 133. Low Larkspur

TALL WOOD LARKSPUR *(Delphinium occidentale)*, Fig. 134, is usually associated with aspen and spruce groves. It blooms in mid-summer with numerous racemes of purple and dark-blue flowers. This is a showy and beautiful plant. It grows 4 to 6 feet tall with several erect side branches surrounding the main stem. The individual blossoms are about an inch wide. It is not as poisonous as the above species.

Fig. 134. Tall Wood Larkspur

WHITE WATER CROWFOOT *(Ranunculus aquatilis)*, Fig. 135, grows mostly submersed in slow moving streams. The waxy-white flowers, ½ inch across, are projected above the surface of the water on short, stiff stems. In June, July, and August they frequently cover large surfaces of the water with a white mass of bloom. The leaves are limp and collapsing when removed from the water.

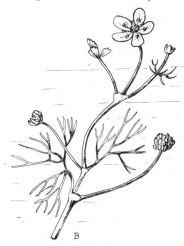

Fig. 135. White Water Crowfoot

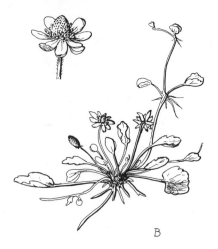

136. Rocky Mountain Buttercup

ROCKY MOUNTAIN BUTTER-CUP *(Ranunculus cymbalaria)*, Fig. 136, is a low, creeping plant that grows in marshy places, often in saline or alkaline soil. Its yellow, shiny blossoms are about ½ inch across and come at the top of 2 inch scapes. The long, stoloniferous runners may be a foot long. It blooms from May to September.

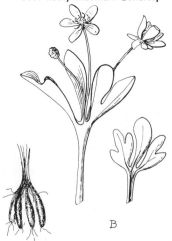

Fig. 137. Sagebrush Buttercup

SAGEBRUSH BUTTERCUP *(Ranunculus jovis)*, Fig. 137, is an early flowering, succulent plant that sends up leaves and waxy blossoms very early in the spring while the ground is still wet from melting snow. The leaves show a great deal of variation in shape but all are divided to the base. The blossoms are ½ to 1 inch in diameter, five or six petaled, and golden yellow. It is adapted to a wide variation in elevation and can be found on our foothills in April and in the high mountains beside melting snowdrifts in June and July.

Fig. 138. Macoun Buttercup

MACOUN BUTTERCUP *(Ranunculus macounii)*, Fig. 138, is a perennial with stout stems that frequently root at the nodes. It grows in marshy areas at 7,000 to 8,000 feet elevation and is 10 to 36 inches tall. The blossoms are about 1 inch in diameter, five petaled, clawed, yellow and have the smooth waxen sheen characteristic of buttercups. It blooms in May, June and July. Its fruit is an achene with a short, straight beak.

STRAIGHT-BEAK BUTTER-
CUP *(Ranunculus orthorhynchus)*,
Fig. 139, grows up to 20 inches
tall and blooms in meadows in May
and June. The blossoms stand
erect, above the leaves and in
blooming season present a solid
mass of color. The petals are bright
yellow, shiny on top, duller on the
underside. They are sometimes
tinged with red. The flowers are
larger than those of *R. macounii*
and the fruit has a long straight
beak.

Fig. 139. Straight-Beak Buttercup

MEADOW RUE *(Thalictrum
fendleri)*, Fig. 140, can be found
growing on damp hillsides at high
elevations. It is frequently associated and sometimes confused with
COLUMBINE *(Aquilegia)*. However, only their leaves and habit of
growth are similar. Individual
Thalictrum plants bear either pistillate flowers, that are erect and
bristly, or staminate flowers, that
are pendulant and soft. The plant
grows 12 to 30 inches tall. ALPINE
MEADOW RUE *(T. alpinum)*
grows in artic regions. It is similar
to *T. fendleri* but is smaller and
individual flowers have both stamens and pistils.

Fig. 140. Meadow Rue

POPPY FAMILY

Members of the poppy family
have clear, milky or sometimes yellow, acrid sap. Most of them have
two sepals that fall off at blooming
time. PRICKLY POPPY *(Arge-
mone munita)*, Fig. 141, is well
named. Its grayish leaves and stems
are thickly armed with sharp,
flexible spines that serve as formid-
able protection. It is erect, branched and grows 2 to 3 feet high on
dry, gravelly hillsides. The flowers
are white, terminal and quite lovely.

Fig. 141. Prickly Poppy

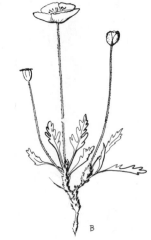

Fig. 142. Wild Poppy

WILD POPPY *(Papaver radicatum)*, Fig. 142, grows in loose shale soil above the timber line and rarely below 10,000 feet in the Uinta Mountains. The leaves are basal and the flowers are borne at the top of 6 to 8 inch scapes that are densely covered with stiff black hairs. Its flowers are 1 to 2½ inches across, yellow or rarely white with numerous yellow stamens. The fruit is a capsule that, at maturity, opens small pores just under the stigma. From these the seeds are scattered whenever the plant is shaken.

Fig. 143. Field Poppy

FIELD POPPY *(Roemeria refracta)*, Fig. 143, was introduced from the Mediterranean area and has become established here. Its 2½ inch bright-orange petals are jet black at the base with a narrow edge of white between the two colors. It grows about 12 inches tall on our foothills. It has become a weed in wheat fields on the west side of Cache Valley.

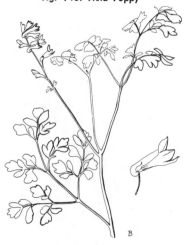

Fig. 144. Golden Corydalis

FUMITORY FAMILY

The fumitory family is made up of herbaceous plants with watery juice and dissected leaves. The flowers are irregular, perfect and have four petals and two sepals. GOLDEN CORYDALIS *(Corydalis aurea)*, Fig. 144, grows in most of the canyons in the Wasatch Mountains. It blooms in May and again in August with short racemes of golden-yellow flowers. It is 10 to 12 inches tall.

STEERSHEAD BLEEDING-HEART *(Dicentra uniflora)*, Fig. 145, is only 2 to 3 inches tall and can easily be overlooked. It blooms on hillsides while the soil is still moist in the spring. The flowers are dusty pinkish lavender and white with dark markings. It can be found in our mountains at elevations from 4,700 to 9,000 feet. They are interesting enough to make hunting for them worthwhile.

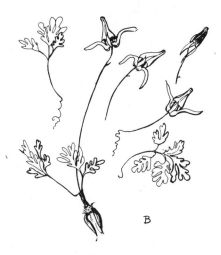

Fig. 145. Steershead Bleedingheart

MUSTARD FAMILY

The mustard family is a large one with many species represented in our area. They have acrid, watery sap, alternate leaves and four petals. The flowers are frequently less conspicuous than the fruit. ROCK CRESS *(Arabis holboellii)*, Fig. 146, grows 1 to 2 feet high with slender racemes of pinkish flowers from June to August. It grows on high mountains in dry, gravelly soil. *Arabis glabra* is very similar but grows in moist, wooded areas and its leaves are glabrous. It blooms in summer. *A. microphylla* blooms from June to September in high dry mountainsides. It has basal leaves and small white flowers on a 6 to 8 inch stem that resembles *A. holboellii*.

Fig. 146. Rock Cress

BIRD RAPE *(Brassica rapa)*, Fig. 147, is one of the two species of mustard plants that cover our fields with yellow bloom in the spring. It is a biennial 12 to 30 inches high, with stiff woody stems and numerous branches. The upper leaves have a smooth, waxy surface and clasp the stem. It blooms in May and June with clear-yellow blossoms about ½ inch in diameter.

Fig. 147. Bird Rape

Fig. 148. Black Mustard

BLACK MUSTARD *(Brassica nigra)*, Fig. 148, grows twice as tall as *B. rapa*, and it blooms a little later in the season. The leaves are wider and are not clasping. Otherwise, they are very similar. Black mustard is generally accepted as the mustard of the New Testament parable. Both species were introduced from Europe by Franciscan missionaries more than 100 years ago.

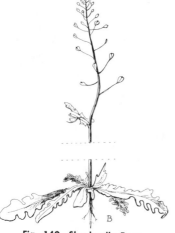

Fig. 149. Shepherd's Purse

SHEPHERD'S PURSE *(Capsella bursa-pastoris)*, Fig. 149, has a Latin name that means small box, referring to its interesting heart-shaped seed capsules. It grows in dry places at lower elevations and blooms in April. It is rarely more than 14 inches tall. The flowers are small and white. Its leaves are rough, pubescent, and have a paper-like stiffness.

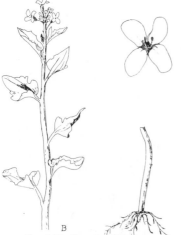

Fig. 150. Heartleaf Bittercress

HEARTLEAF BITTERCRESS *(Cardamine cordifolia)*, Fig. 150, is found in shallow water of cold mountain streams, sometimes growing in depressions and cracks of rocks that are midstream. It grows 14 to 20 inches high, is erect and sometimes branched. The leaves are smooth, heart-shaped, and vivid green. Its flowers are about ½ inch across, snow white and very attractive. It blooms in July and August.

WHITETOP *(Cardaria draba)*, Fig. 151, is an attractive but noxious weed on ditchbanks or roadsides. It grows in thick stands with erect or ascending stems 8 to 20 inches high. They are branched at the inflorescence. The leaves are green and close set. Its flowers are small and white and come in May and June.

Fig. 151. Whitetop

TANSY LEAFED MUSTARD *(Descurainia pinnata)*, Fig. 152, is an annual that grows on dry hillsides high in our mountains. The fine lacy quality of its fresh green leaves and yellow blossoms set it apart. They grow about 14 inches tall and in mass are very showy. As the seeds mature, however, it becomes ragged and inconspicuous. FLIXWEED TANSY MUSTARD *(Descuraina sophia)* is very similar except that the leaves are more finely cut.

Fig 152. Tansy Leafed Mustard

WALLFLOWER *(Erysimum capitatum)*, Fig. 153, is the most beautiful native member of the mustard family in our area. It has racemes of flowers at the apex of single upright stems 12 to 18 inches high. The blossoms are ¾ inch across, clear yellow to orange yellow and have a spicy carnation-like fragrance. They grow in dry, gravelly situations on our foothills and at middle elevations. They bloom in May and June. Unfortunately the plant is easily uprooted when the flower is picked and it is therefore becoming rare.

Fig. 153. Wallflower

Fig. 154. Woad

Fig. 155. Water Cress

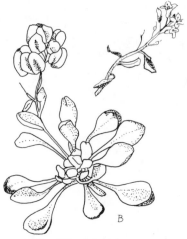

Fig. 156. Twinpod

WOAD *(Isatis tinctoria)*, Fig. 154, covers many of our foothills with golden-yellow color in the spring. It grows 4 to 12 inches high, is glabrous, and sometimes has a whitish wax on the stems and leaves. The name *tinctoria* refers to the dark fruit from which blue dye was formerly made. A native of Europe, it is now naturalized in many parts of the United States.

WATERCRESS *(Nasturtium officinale* or *Rorippa nasturtium-aquaticum)*, Fig. 155, is one of the best known plants in our flora and one of the first that came to historical notice. Coronado found it in 1541 and the Lewis and Clark expedition (1804-1806) gathered it in Oregon. Its succulent, spicy leaves and stems always seem to have been prized as an item of diet. It grows in ponds and slow moving streams where it stays green all winter. The small white flowers come from May to September.

TWINPOD *(Physaria australis)*, Fig. 156, can be found on dry, gravelly hillsides in April, blooming with yellow flowers about ½ inch in diameter. These are followed in July with cream or rose-colored inflated pods, more conspicuous than the flowers. The surfaces of the stems and leaves are covered with microscopic, stiff, hairy pubescence arranged in numerous whorls to form a star-like pattern. This can be seen easily with a hand lens. TWINPOD *(Physaria cambersii)* is a similar plant with the two parts of its inflated pods unequal in size.

CAPER FAMILY

PINK BEE FLOWER *(Cleome serrulata)*, Fig. 157, grows in a showy branching clump. In July and August it has magenta-pink blossoms at the ends of stems 30 to 40 inches high. Its fruit is a many seeded capsule. YELLOW BEE FLOWER *(Cleome lutea)* is similar but grows half as tall, has lower leaves made up of five to seven parts rather than three, and has yellow flowers. Both are annuals that grow in open, sandy, fairly moist areas.

Fig. 157. Pink Bee Flower

STONECROP FAMILY

STONECROP *(Sedum debile)*, Fig. 158, like most members of the stonecrop family, has smooth, thick, succulent leaves and stems which aid in storing water for the plant. It grows 4 to 6 inches in dry gravelly soil on mountain ridges. Its leaves are opposite and gray green with touches of rose at the base. NARROW-PETALED STONE-CROP *(Sedum stenopetalum)* is similar to *S. debile* but has leaves that are alternate, greener and longer.

Fig. 158. Stonecrop

SAXIFRAGE FAMILY

ALUM ROOT — WILD COR-ALBELLS *(Heuchera rubescens)*, Fig. 159, grows in rock crevices, often on the sheer face of canyon cliffs. Its blossoms are borne on wiry stems in spike-like racemes 12 to 15 inches long. The brownish pink flowers have red stamens extending beyond the corolla. It blooms in June. LITTLELEAF ALUMROOT *(Heuchera parvifolia)* has a green blossom but otherwise closely resembles *H. rubecens*.

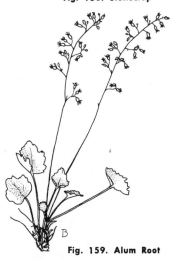

Fig. 159. Alum Root

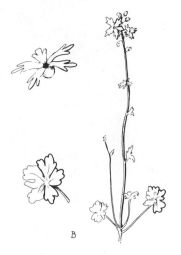

Fig| 160. Woodland Star

WOODLAND STAR (*Lithophragma glabra* or *L. bulbifera* of older manuals), Fig. 160, and *L. parviflora* not only share a common name but closely resemble each other. Both are glandular pubescent, have white or pinkish flowers and grow in shady places. *L. glabra* is generally shorter. It has pink bulblets in the axils and blooms April to June. It grows at higher elevations.

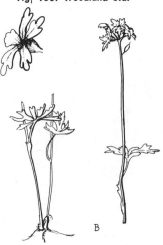

Fig. 161. Woodland Star

WOODLAND STAR (*Lithophragma parvifolia*), Fig. 161, is the species we find, generally, in our lower canyons and on foothills. It grows 10 to 12 inches tall and prefers rocky places. It is the sturdier of the two species and has well developed stem leaves. It blooms in May and June. The blossoms of both species are about ¾ inch across. Watch for both these attractive little flowers in open woods, under tall trees. *Lithophragma* is of Greek origin meaning rock and fence, referring to the habitat.

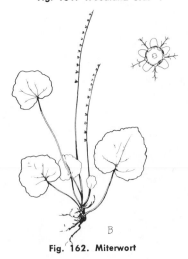

Fig. 162. Miterwort

MITERWORT (*Mitella stenopetala*), Fig. 162, can be found blooming in May and June in bogs where there is rich soil and shade. It has basal leaves that are smooth and dark green. The racemes of small, white flowers have as many as twenty blossoms on a wiry stem about 12 inches tall. It grows at elevations between 8,500 and 12,000 feet throughout our mountains.

ROCKY MOUNTAIN GRASS OF PARNASSUS *(Parnassia fimbriata)*, Fig. 163, grows from short rootstocks. The flower scape is up to 12 inches high with a single satin textured white blossom at the top. The sides of the petals are delicately fringed at their base. Its leaves are dark green, smooth and shiny. They can be found growing in bogs and on the banks of streams at elevations from 8,500 feet upward. They bloom from July to September.

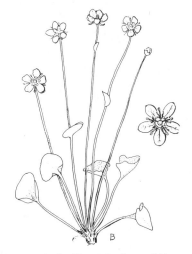

Fig. 163. Rocky Mountain Grass of Parnassus

DIAMOND LEAF SAXIFRAGE *(Saxifraga rhomboidea)*, Fig. 164, can be found high in our mountains on moist, rocky banks and alpine slopes. It blooms in June and July with tight clusters of ½ inch flowers at the top of smooth, green stems. The petals are white and the stamens reddish brown. The leaves are fleshy, very smooth and, as their common name implies, diamond shaped.

Fig. 164. Diamond Leaf Saxifrage

ROSE FAMILY

The rose family is one of the largest and most familiar families in our flora. Some of its most conspicuous genera include: apple, rose, hawthorn, strawberry, etc. WILD STRAWBERRY *(Fragaria vesca)*, Fig. 165, will be easily recognized because of its resemblance to the domestic strawberry. You can find this plant growing in forest clearings and open areas in our mountains between 7,000 and 8,000-foot elevation. It grows only a few inches high, has soft, thin leaves; white blossom ¾ inch across and small, bright-red fruit that is sweet and delicious. It blooms in May and the fruit ripens in early summer.

Fig. 165. Wild Strawberry

Fig. 166. Largeleaf Avens

LARGELEAF AVENS *(Geum macrophyllum)*, Fig. 166, grows in wet meadows and on stream banks, mostly above 7,000 feet elevation. It is an erect, bristly-hairy plant, much-branched and 3 feet high. The ½ inch yellow flowers are followed quickly by the fruits. It blooms from May to August.

Fig. 167. Gordon's Ivesia

GORDON'S IVESIA *(Ivesia gordoni)*, Fig. 167, is found on rocky slopes above the timber line in both the Wasatch and Uinta Mountains. It grows about 12 inches high from a thick rootstock. The small, clustered blossoms are yellow. The leaves are mostly basal and are smooth and green.

Fig. 168. Silverweed Cinquefoil

Cinquefoil means five fingers and is the common name of the genus *Potentilla*. This is one of the most abundant plants in the Rockies and one of the most widely scattered. Cinquefoils are native to Europe, Asia and most of North America. They are mostly five petaled and nearly all have yellow flowers. SILVERWEED CINQUEFOIL *(Potentilla anserina)*, Fig. 168, is called GOOSE TANSY in England. It usually grows in wet, saline soil. It is rarely more than 7 inches tall and has long, creeping, edible stolens. The yellow flowers are about an inch in diameter and attractive. They bloom from April to October. Its leaves, that are dark green above and silvery pubescent beneath, are very beautiful.

STICKY CINQUEFOIL (*Potentilla glandulosa*), Fig. 169, has erect, branching, stiff stems 8 inches tall. It is few flowered with pale yellow satin-smooth ¾ inch blossoms at the ends of the branches. It grows on open mountain slopes. Numerous glands on the leaves make them sticky to the touch. *Potentilla arguta* is usually larger and it has coarser leaves. The flowers are similar but come in a more compact head and are paler in color. It grows 18 inches high in open woods.

Fig. 169. Sticky Cinquefoil

CINQUEFOIL (*Potentilla gracilis*), Fig. 170, grows in moist places on mountain sides and stream banks at high elevations. It has an upright, slender habit of growth and at full height is about 24 inches. Like *P. anserina* its leaves have heavy gray pubescence on the underside that contrasts sharply with the dark green on the top. The flowers are yellow and about ½ inch in diameter.

Fig. 170. Cinquefoil

SIBBALDIA (*Sibbaldia procumbens*), Fig. 171, was named for Robert Sibbald, a Scotch botanist. It is a densely tufted, procumbent, perennial plant, common in the high Uintas. It is one of the five species found at the Arctic and alpine regions of the northern hemisphere. It has small yellow blossoms in June and July.

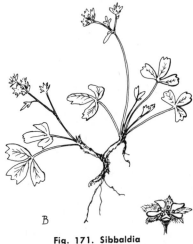

Fig. 171. Sibbaldia

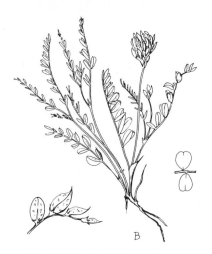

Fig. 172. Beckwith's Astragalus

Fig. 173. Loco Weed

Fig. 174. Fineleaf Astragalus

PEA FAMILY

Legumes, members of the pea family, include beans, peas, clovers, etc. Ours have the characteristic pea-shaped blossoms and legume pods. Their leaves are compound. *Astragalus* is a common legume genus in our area. As a group, they are quite dangerous to livestock. Animals seem to develop an addiction to the plant which produces a type of incurable insanity called locoing. BECKWITH'S ASTRAGALUS *(Astragalus beckwithii)*, Fig. 172, grows in clumps 6 to 8 inches high on dry gravelly slopes. It blooms in June with racemes of flowers that may be blue, yellow or lavender. At maturity the pods are yellow with pale brown mottling.

LOCO WEED *(Astragalus cibarius)*, Fig. 173, produces several flowering stems from a long, stout, taproot. The flowers are whitish to magenta and the leaves are gray green. Both the leaves and seed pods are glabrous. They can be found blooming in April and May on dry, gravelly hillsides.

FINELEAF ASTRAGALUS *(Astragalus diversifolius)*, Fig. 174, has a more upright habit than most species of astragalus. It has thin, ridged 14 inch stems that are four-sided and hollow. They grow from a thick perennial crown. The stems and leaves are pubescent and gray green. The flowers are numerous and pinkish white. They grow in thick, close growing clumps in dry, rocky soil and bloom in May and June. Like most other members of the *Astragalus* genus, they are foothill inhabitants.

DRUMMOND'S MILKVETCH
(Astragalus eurekensis), Fig. 175, is common in dry, gravelly, loam in the Provo area and westward. It is 4 inches high and densely branched from a taproot. Its leaves, stems and seed pods are covered with a fine gray pubescence. The flowers are white with a touch of blue on the keel.

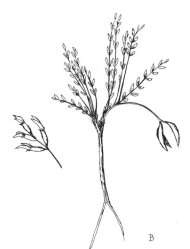

Fig. 175. Drummond's Milkvetch

HORN LOCOWEED *(Astragalus miser)*, Fig. 176, grows in a spreading clump 8 inches high and 12 inches across. The leaves are green with white pubescence and the blossoms are white to yellowish with violet markings on the keel. It grows on dry hillsides and blooms in May and June. MOTTLED RATTLEWEED *(Astragalus lentiginosus)* has blossoms that are similar in shape and may be either violet blue or pale yellow. The leaves are rounder at the ends and the seed pods are broad with two compartments. The nodes closely resemble *A. miser*.

Fig. 176. Horn Locoweed

PINK LADY SLIPPER *(Astragalus utahensis)*, Fig. 177, is one of the most attractive species we have. It grows flat on the ground in a circular mat about 14 inches in diameter. The leaves are gray, woolly-pubescent. In April and May it has racemes of bright magenta flowers at the end of leafless stems. The blossoms are about 1 inch long and ½ inch wide. The seed pods are so pubescent that they resemble bits of white fur. WOOLLYPOD *(A. purshii)* closely resembles *A. utahensis*, but the leaves on *A. purshii* are more pointed, the flowers are more purple—some are bi-colored. The seed pods are longer.

Fig. 177. Pink Lady Slipper

Fig. 178. American Licorice

Fig. 179. Northern Sweet Broom

Fig. 180. Annual Lupine

AMERICAN LICORICE *(Glycyrrhiza lepidota)*, Fig. 178, is an erect plant 1 to 3 feet high with spikes of small yellowish-white flowers that bloom May to August. These are followed by brown pods covered with hooked prickles. They grow in sand and gravel on stream banks and other areas where the soil is damp. It is a native of America, related to the European species *(Glycyrrhiza glabra)* from which licorice flavoring is obtained.

NORTHERN SWEET BROOM *(Hedysarum boreale)*, Fig. 179, can be found on dry hillsides growing in a compact bushy clump about 2 feet high. The blossoms are bright rose pink and very showy. The leaves are green above and grayish on the underside.

Lupines are among our best known mountain plants. Most of them grow at lower elevations, though a few may be found up to 10,000 feet. Of about 200 species found in this country, most of them are native to the West. The name "Lupine" is Latin, meaning wolf and was given to an European species 20 centuries ago. It was then thought that the plant robbed the soil. Lupine is called "Blue Bonnett" in Texas where it is the state flower. ANNUAL LUPINE *(Lupinus kingii)*, Fig. 180, grows in dry, sandy soil and blooms in July. The plants are about 6 inches high. Its leaves are gray green and very pubescent. The blossoms are blue with a white keel. Mature seed stalks and blooming stalks may be found on the same plant.

SPURRED LUPINE *(Lupinus caudatus)*, Fig. 181, is a perennial common in our dry rocky foothills. It grows in clumps and has racemes of blue-purple or (rarely) white blossoms and is about 20 inches tall. Its leaves and stems are silky pubescent and gray green. SILKY LUPINE *(Lupinus sericeus)* is very similar except that its blossoms range through rose, white, cream and blue purple. It grows a little taller than *Lupinus caudatus* and the individual blossoms are not spurred. The seed pods are also smaller.

Fig. 181. Spurred Lupine

MOUNTAIN THERMOPSIS *(Thermopsis montana)*, Fig. 182, grows in upright clumps and has stems 2 feet high. The racemes are loosely flowered with clear, lemon yellow blossoms nearly an inch long. The leaves are dark green and lightly pubescent beneath. It grows on stream banks and in moist woods. Its seed pods are erect and straight.

Fig. 182. Mountain Thermopsis

Trifolium is a Latin name referring to the three leaflets that are characteristic of clover. Its blossoms are in heads or short spikes. LONG-STALKED CLOVER *(Trifolium longipes)*, Fig. 183, is a perennial with a creeping rootstalk. Its stems are erect and up to 14 inches high. It can be found blooming in mountain meadows and on stream banks from June to September. The flowers are white.

Fig. 183. Long-Stalked Clover

Fig. 184. Dwarf Clover

Fig. 185. Red Clover

Fig. 186. Storksbill

DWARF CLOVER (*Trifolium nanum*), Fig. 184, forms dense, low mats on ridges and talus slopes above the timber line in the Uinta mountains. It blooms in July and August with slender blossoms ¾ inch long. The leaves are green, almost glabrous and have a deep fold down the center. The perennial rootstalk is woody and has defoliating bark.

RED CLOVER (*Trifolium pratense*), Fig. 185, grows up to 1 foot high, is spreading and more or less erect. The bright-rose blossoms grow at the apex of round, wiry stems and are more than an inch in diameter. This is native to Europe and has become widely naturalized. Clover is dependent upon bumblebees for pollination since no other insect is strong enough to spring open the blossom and get at the pollen and stigma.

GERANIUM FAMILY

STORKSBILL, FILAREE (*Erodium cicutarium*), Fig. 186, is low and spreading from a central taproot. The leaves are rich green and ferny. The blossoms are lilac pink. It blooms on our foothills from May to November. It is an immigrant from the Mediterranean region that was brought to California for its forage value by Franciscan missionaries. It derives its name from a Greek word meaning heron, referring to the resemblance of its immature seeds to that bird. Its seeds when mature look like small corkscrews and respond to moisture changes by coiling and uncoiling, thus securing the seed in the earth or in an animal's fur for transportation.

WILD PINK GERANIUM
(Geranium fremontii), Fig. 187, has
many characteristics reminiscent of
our domestic garden geraniums,
which belong to the same family.
It is a handsome, round, bushy
plant 16 inches to 30 inches high
with numerous rose-pink flowers
and dark-green leaves. It blooms
from May to September and can be
found growing on hillsides in elevations between 6,500 and 11,500
feet. WILD WHITE GERANIUM
(Geranium richardsonii) is very
similar but has white flowers with
delicate pinkish veins. It prefers
moist situations. When ripe, the
long, pointed seed pods of both
species split from the bottom up
with force enough to scatter the
seeds over a wide area.

Fig. 187. Wild Pink Geranium

FLAX FAMILY

WILD BLUE FLAX *(Linum
lewisii)*, Fig. 188, is a delicate, erect
plant 1 to 2 feet high. Several stems
grow from a single crown and produce fragile, sky-blue flowers, 1
inch or more across, usually one at
a time, from a loose raceme. The
stems contain long fibers similar to
those used in making linen but
somewhat less strong. They grow
on dry, gravelly hillsides between
4,500 and 9,500-foot elevation.

Fig. 188. Wild Blue Flax

YELLOW FLAX *(Linum kingii)*,
Fig. 189, has a similar habit of
growth but is more branched and
shorter. The flowers are a little
smaller and are yellow. They grow
only at high elevations.

Fig. 189. Yellow Flax

MALLOW FAMILY

Fig. 190. Wild Hollyhock

WILD HOLLYHOCK *(Iliamna rivularis)*, Fig. 190, is a magnificent plant with many strong, erect, branching stems terminating in loose racemes of flowers from June to August. It grows 3 to 6 feet high on stream banks, mountain slopes and in meadows at middle elevations in our mountains. The blossoms are 2 inches or more in diameter, delicate pink or white with pom-poms of yellow stamens in the center.

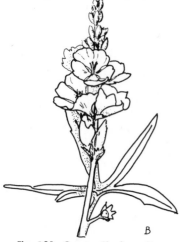

Fig. 191. Oregon Checkermallow

OREGON CHECKERMALLOW *(Sidalcea oregana)*, Fig. 191, is an erect perennial 3 to 5 feet tall with spike-like racemes or rose-pink flowers each an inch wide. They grow in mountain meadows and on moist mountain sides. They bloom June to September.

Fig. 192. Scarlet Globemallow

SCARLET GLOBEMALLOW *(Sphaeralcea munroana)*, Fig. 192, grows on dry hillsides in association with sagebrush. It has one to several stiff, erect stems 2½ feet high. It blooms from May to September with flowers that range in color from tangerine to brick red. Its leaves have a rough, sandpaper texture. *Sphaeralcea coccinea* is similar but the leaves are deeply divided and the stems are somewhat shorter. Both plants grow in disturbed areas.

CHEESES *(Malva neglecta)*, Fig. 193, received its common name from the shape of the seed which resembles an uncut cheese. It is a low, spreading annual with stems 12 to 14 inches long. The blossoms are an inch wide and pink or white with pink veins. It blooms from May to September.

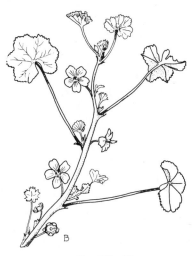

Fig. 193. Cheeses

ST. JOHN'S WORT FAMILY

ST. JOHN'S WORT *(Hypericum formosum* var. *scouleri)*, Fig. 194, grows 6 to 36 inch erect stems from rhizomes. It can be found along stream banks in limestone gravel in elevations between 5,000 and 9,000 feet. The yellow flowers are a little more than ½ inch across. It has tiny black dots all around the margins of the flowers and leaves and translucent dots over the surface of the leaves. The buds are red. They bloom from July to September.

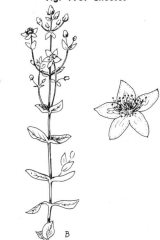

Fig. 194. St. John's Wort

VIOLET FAMILY

Violets generally have two types of blossoms: The early, showy ones are followed by rather inconspicuous fertile ones. The seedpods of all violets burst at maturity with such suddenness that seed is scattered for considerable distances. BLUE VIOLET *(Viola adunca)*, Fig. 195, has a violet-blue flower with fine black markings in the white throat. The plants produce short stems and grow in rich, damp soil. It is found in elevations between 5,000 and 11,500 feet and blooms from May to July.

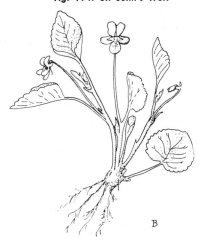

Fig. 195. Blue Violet

Fig. 196. Western Pansy Violet

WESTERN PANSY VIOLET *(Viola beckwithii)*, Fig. 196, is one of the earliest to bloom in our area. It produces leaves and blossoms before the winter moisture has left the ground, which may be any time from March to May, depending upon the earliness of the season. They are low plants, arising from short rootstocks. The blossoms are an inch across with upper petals that are deep red violet, while the lower ones are white or pale lavender with a yellow base. The leaves are dark green. They grow in open fields on our foothills but are disappearing where urbanization has encroached on their habitat.

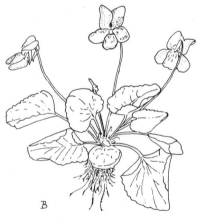

Fig. 197. Bog Violet

BOG VIOLET *(Viola nephrophylla)*, Fig. 197, is widely distributed in our mountains, wherever there is rich wet soil. It is a compact stemless plant, that grows 6 inches tall from a stout, rather fleshy rootstock. The flowers are borne on slender scapes and are pale blue with dark purple markings in the throat. The lower petals are bearded with slender hairs. They bloom from April to June.

Fig. 198. Yellow Mountain Violet

YELLOW MOUNTAIN VIOLET *(Viola purpurea)*, Fig. 198, grows on dry, gravelly foothills and up to about 11,000 foot elevations. The leaves are pointed and roughly wedge-shaped. The buds are brown and the blossoms are lemon yellow with brown on the backs of the upper petals. *NUTTALL VIOLET (Viola nuttallii)* which grows in the Uinta Mountains is similar to *V. purpurea* but does not have the brown color on the back of the petals.

BLAZING-STAR FAMILY

BLAZING-STAR *(Mentzelia laevicaulis)*, Fig. 199, is a coarse, branching plant that grows 1 to 3 feet high on gravel banks and in disturbed areas. The leaves are sparse, rough and gray green. The plant would be completely unimpressive were it not for its truly spectacular blossoms. It blooms from June to September. The flowers are frequently 5 inches in diameter with five petals that range in color from rich yellow to nearly white. The outer five stamens are often petal-like.

Fig. 199. Blazing-Star

CACTUS FAMILY

The cactus family is a large one that is essentially associated with drier regions than ours, but some genera do occur in our area. They are represented here by PRICKLY PEAR *(Opuntia rhodantha)*, Fig. 200. It can be found in full flower from April to June on stony slopes and gravelly washes in elevations between 5,000 and 6,100 feet. The yellow flowers have a waxy sheen and are 2 inches in diameter. They become rose pink as they fade. The fruit is fleshy and many seeded.

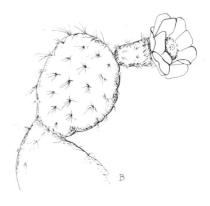

Fig. 200. Pricky Pear

EVENING PRIMROSE FAMILY

FIREWEED *(Epilobium angustifolium)*, Fig. 201, has one of the widest distributions of any plant in the world. It is handsome with 2 to 8 foot terminal racemes of lilac rose flowers that bloom from July to September. They grow in moist areas that have been burned over or disturbed. The fruit develops rapidly and buds, flowers and mature fruit appear on the same plant.

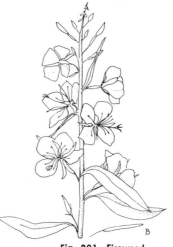

Fig. 201. Fireweed

Fig. 202. Evening Primrose

EVENING PRIMROSE *(Oenothera caespitosa)*, Fig. 202, is the most beautiful of our evening primroses. It grows close to the ground with a rosette of basal leaves and stemless flowers on long floral tubes. It blooms in late evening and fades the following morning. The blossoms are nearly 4 inches across, snow white, turning pink with age. They are magnificently fragrant. It can be found on dry, sandy hillsides at lower and middle elevations. It blooms from May to July.

Fig. 203. Sun Cups

SUN CUPS *(Oenothera heterantha)*, Fig. 203, grows in wet mountain meadows. It has leaves 4 to 6 inches long radiating from a strong central taproot. It is about 2 inches high. The blossoms are clear yellow and satin textured. The leaves are green, tinged with rose. It blooms in June and July. Another SUN CUP *(Oenothera tanacetifolia)* is similar but has much-divided, pinnatifid leaves.

Fig. 204. Hooker Evening Primrose

HOOKER EVENING PRIMROSE *(Oenothera hookeri)*, Fig. 204, is a well formed, branching perennial 2 to 4 feet high. In the evening it produces fragrant, satiny yellow blossoms about 3 inches in diameter. They fade when the sun strikes them the following day. Their yellow pollen is connected by thread-like filaments that cling to insects and thus aid in their pollination. It grows in moist places mostly above 5,100 feet and blooms from July until October.

PALE EVENING PRIMROSE *(Oenothera pallida)*, Fig. 205, is a perennial that grows about 20 inches tall and has creeping rootstalks. Its stems are white and exfoliating. The flowers, that are about 2½ inches across, are white, turning rose as they fade. They, like other evening primroses, bloom at night and are very fragrant. Look for them on dry, sandy hillsides and washes.

Fig. 205. Pale Evening Primrose

DESERT EVENING PRIM-ROSE *(Oenothera trichocalyx)*, Fig. 206, is an annual that grows on the dry, sandy parts of our foothills. The numerous 12 inch stems from a short stem have whitish exfoliating epidermis as they mature. It blooms in June and July with 1½ inch flowers that have tissue thin, white petals that turn rose pink with age. The leaves are gray green and pubescent.

Fig. 206. Desert Evening Primrose

WILD FUCHSIA *(Zauschneria garrettii)*, Fig. 207, has one to many stems 6 to 8 inches high, from a single crown. It can be found on dry, gravelly slopes at high elevations in our canyons. The stems are somewhat woody and have exfoliating epidermis. The blossoms, that are about 1½ inches long, are scarlet red. The scarlet tube ends in eight appendages with four being erect and four below spreading slightly. It blooms in July and August.

Fig. 207. Wild Fuchsia

WATER MILFOIL FAMILY

AMERICAN MILFOIL *(Myrio-phyllum spicatum)*, Fig. 208, is a water plant that grows submersed in shallow parts of mountain lakes and ponds. It is notable for its beautiful foliage which is arranged in whorls around its smooth, hollow stem. The leaves are green and the stem is green touched with rose. The blossoms are inconspicuous.

Fig. 208. American Milfoil

PARSLEY FAMILY

Members of this family take their name from their type of inflorescence — the umbel. The individual flowers are generally small but extremely interesting when viewed through a hand lens. Some are poisonous, which is reason enough to treat all of them with caution until positive identification has been made. All are quite aromatic. SMALL-LEAF ANGELICA *(Angelica pinnata)*, Fig. 209, is an erect, slender plant, 2 feet high, that can be found in cool, moist, rocky places high in the mountains. Its flowers are white with dark centers. As in all members of this family, the stems are hollow. *Angelica* is Latin alluding to its supposed healing properties.

Fig. 209. Small-leaf Angelica

ANGELICA *(Angelica roseana)*, Fig. 210, has thick, sturdy stems and is a larger, more robust plant than *A. pinnata*. The flowers are white with touches of pink and purple. It grows in wet, rocky ground above the timber line and is common on most of the higher peaks in the Uintas. It blooms in late summer.

Fig. 210. Angelica

WATERHEMLOCK *(Cicuta douglasii)*, Fig. 211, is a handsome and dangerous plant 3 to 7 feet tall. It is a native species and one of the most poisonous plants in Utah. The leaves and roots supply excellent clues to its identification. In the leaves, the side veins terminate at the indented part of the margin and not to the tip of the tooth. The root is a horizontally chambered rootstock that is not found in any other species. It grows in marshes and wet areas and has white flowers from June to August. The fruit is globose with low ribs.

Fig. 211. Waterhemlock

POISONHEMLOCK *(Conium maculatum)*, Fig. 212, was introduced from Europe and grows in moist to dry ground in open fields and on ditch banks. It grows 5 to 10 feet tall and has coarse, green stems with purple spots. The leaves are thrice compound and the blossoms are small, white and lacy. It has minute fruit, with prominent ribs, slightly laterally compressed. All parts of this plant are poisonous.

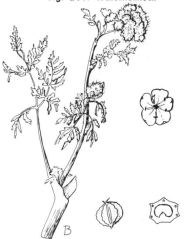

Fig. 212. Poisonhemlock

CYMOPTERUS *(Cymopterus longipes)*, Fig. 213, is a ground hugging herb with a fleshy, sheathed taproot and pale gray-green leaves. It makes its appearance very early in the spring on our foothills. The blossoms are yellow and lacy. The specific name refers to the foot of the plant which elongates considerably after the leaves first appear. *Cymopterus ibapensis* is very similar except that its blossoms are white.

Fig. 213.   Cymopterus

Fig. 214. Cow Parsnip

COW PARSNIP *(Heracleum lanatum)*, Fig. 214, is impressive for its size as well as its beauty. It grows 3 to 10 feet high with thick, branching stems and leaves that are sometimes more than 20 inches across. The umbels of flowers are white with those on the outside being irregular. The outer petals are much enlarged and often two-toothed. It grows in moist, partly shaded places below 9,000 feet elevation and blooms in mid-summer.

Fig. 215. Wild Carrot

WILD CARROT *(Lomatium dissectum)*, Fig. 215, is common in early spring in our canyons and on our foothills. Its leaves and blossoms appear in April and May. It is a sturdy, vigorous plant 1 to 3 feet high that thrives in rocky, open places. The leaves are rich green and the blossoms greenish yellow sometimes tinged with purple. The plant is very aromatic.

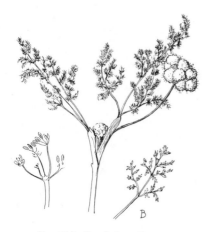

Fig. 216. Gray's Lomatium

GRAY'S LOMATIUM *(Lomatium grayii)*, Fig. 216, is a pungent, early spring blooming plant that grows in rocky, dry soil on our foothills. Its leaves are bright fresh green and the flowers are mustard yellow. They grow only a few inches high from a long, thickened tap root. *Pteryxia terebinthina* is so similar that it is difficult to tell the two plants apart in the field except for the leaves (lower right in Fig. 216) which are a little flatter and closely resemble garden parsley.

DESERT PARSLEY *(Lomatium simplex)*, Fig. 217, grows about 14 inches high. Its stems have parallel ribbing and reddish coloring at their base. The flowers are yellow and the fruit is oval. It grows on dry, rocky hill sides. *Lomatium triternatum* is very similar but its mature fruit is narrower and more or less pointed at the ends.

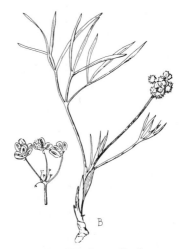

Fig. 217. Desert Parsley

INDIAN PARSNIP *(Orogenia linearifolia)*, Fig. 218, is usually the first plant to bloom in the spring. In March, before its leaves are unfolded, the small white blossoms appear an inch or two above the ground and only a few feet from the melting snow. They have a sweet, slightly offensive odor. Its round, fleshy corms were much prized by the Indians as a spring time addition to their diets.

Fig. 218. Indian Parsnip

SWEET CICELY *(Osmorhiza chilensis)*, Fig. 219, can be found in damp, wooded areas. It is a wiry, branching plant about 2 feet high. The blossoms are very small, greenish white and might easily be overlooked. The mature seeds, however, do not go unnoticed. They are barbed and easily affix themselves to clothing, where their sharp points make their victims very uncomfortable until the irritation is removed. This usually results in another planted seed.

Fig. 219. Sweet Cicely

Fig. 220. Western Sweetanice

WESTERN SWEETANICE

(Osmorhiza occidentalis), Fig. 220, is a stout, erect perennial that grows in cool, moist woods and moist hillsides in our mountains. It reaches a height of about 3 feet and has small umbels of yellowish green flowers in May and June. Crushed leaves have a heavy odor of licorice. The fruits are not bristled as in *O. chilensis*. This is a well formed plant with a pleasing green color. It covers large areas in favorable locations.

Fig. 221. Shinleaf or Alpine Pinedrops

WINTERGREEN FAMILY

SHINLEAF or ALPINE PINE-DROPS *(Pyrola asarifolia)*, Fig. 221, is found growing in rich, moist granite based soil where there is deep shade. It is a creeping plant with leafless scapes 8 to 16 inches tall. The ½ inch, pink, nodding flowers have a waxy texture. The leaves are evergreen, basal, thick and shiny. *Pyrola* is Latin and diminutive of Pyrus which means pear-alluding to the resemblance of its leaves to those of a pear tree. The name "shinleaf" comes from English peasants using them for plasters.

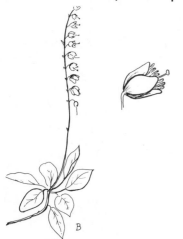

Fig. 222. Sidebells Pyrola

SIDEBELLS PYROLA *(Pyrola secunda)*, Fig. 222, has erect scapes 3 to 6 inches high with many white or pinkish flowers forming a one sided raceme. The buds are erect but as the blossoms open they become nodding. They grow in moist woods and on stream banks in our canyons.

PRIMROSE FAMILY

ANDROSACE *(Androsace fili-formis)*, Fig. 223, is a lacy plant 2 to 4 inches high that inhabits wet places high in our mountains. The leaves are smooth, dark green and glabrous. The flowers are in an umbel at the top of a smooth green stem. They are white with a green calyx. The root is fibrous. Look for them in July and August. *A. septentrionalis* is about 1 inch high, finely pubescent, has a taproot and grows on open slopes. Otherwise, it closely resembles *A. filiformis*.

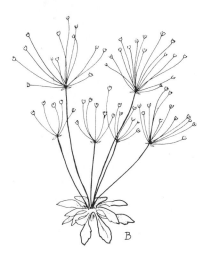

Fig. 223. Androsace

SHOOTING STAR *(Dodecatheon pauciflorum)*, Fig. 224, makes large areas of our mountain meadows rose-colored in May and June when they are in bloom. They are about 12 inches high with individual blossoms a little less than an inch in length. *D. jeffreyi* is similar but may be twice as large. It also has more flowers on each scape and grows at higher elevations. *D. pauciflorum* has long, fused filaments while in *D. jeffreyi* they are absent. Both species are delightfully fragrant.

Fig. 224. Shooting Star

PARRY'S PRIMROSE *(Primula parryi)*, Fig. 225, is a rather rare alpine beauty that grows in wet, rocky places, usually above 10,000 foot elevation. The leaves are thick, smooth, and basal. The blossoms, that are produced on a sturdy scape 4 to 12 inches high, are a little less than an inch across and rose pink with yellow centers. They have a decidedly unpleasant odor. They bloom in July and August. *P. maguirei* is found in rocky slopes in Logan Canyon and resembles *P. parryi*. It is smaller and has fewer flowers on each scape.

Fig. 225. Parry's Primrose

Fig. 226. Fringed Loosestrife

Fig. 227. Showy Gentian

Fig. 228. Rocky Mountain Pleated Gentian

FRINGED LOOSESTRIFE *(Steironema ciliatum)*, Fig. 226, is a delicate, erect, branching herb 12 to 48 inches tall that can be found in wet, shady places in our canyons. The yellow blossoms are about an inch in diameter. The stems are green, smooth, square, and hollow with touches of rose at the axils of the leaves. The name *ciliatum* refers to the fine pubescence on the petioles and at the base and margins of the leaves.

GENTIAN FAMILY

SHOWY GENTIAN *(Frasera speciosa)*, Fig. 227, is a biennial that sends up an erect, sturdy stem from 3 to 6 feet tall from a large taproot. The basal leaves are large, dense, and strap-shaped. On the stems they are smaller and whorled. Racemes of greenish-white flowers, 1½ inches across and spotted with purple, are produced at the axils of the upper leaves to make a cone-shaped plant. It grows in open, usually damp areas above 6,500 foot elevation. They bloom in July and August.

ROCKY MOUNTAIN PLEAT-ED GENTIAN *(Gentiana affinis)*, Fig. 228, is an alpine plant that grows at elevations of 7,000 to 9,500 feet in the Uinta, Bear River, and Wasatch Mountains. It produces several stems 17 inches tall from a single crown. The blossoms come at the tops of the stems and are about 1 inch long. They are a rich dark blue to violet with green tinges on the back of the corolla. It blooms from August to October.

ANNUAL GENTIAN *(Gentiana amarella)*, Fig. 229, is a simple or branched, erect, hollow-stemmed annual, 1 to 16 inches tall that grows in damp places at high elevations. The flowers are ½ inch long and are borne on axillary racemes. The corolla is tubular and pale lavender with dark tips and a white base. Some botanists have divided this species into several groups. They bloom in July and August.

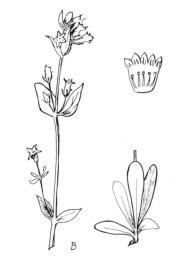

Fig. 229. Annual Gentian

PLEATED GENTIAN *(Gentiana calycosa)*, Fig. 230, is perhaps the handsomest of our gentians. It has a number of smooth, erect or ascending stems from a common crown, each with a blossom at the apex. The flowers are almost 2 inches long and are dark blue with a greenish base. The flowers of gentians are capable of closing very quickly as summer storms come up. The leaves are smooth and glossy. They inhabit alpine meadows and bloom in late summer.

Fig. 230. Pleated Gentian

SMALL PLEATED GENTIAN *(Gentiana fremontii)*, Fig. 231, is an annual or biennial, 2 to 4 inches tall that occurs in our alpine bogs and meadows. The flowers are white with greenish tips and tinges of blue at the base. They bloom in July and August.

Fig. 231. Small Pleated Gentian

Fig. 232. Alpine Bog Swertia

ALPINE BOG SWERTIA *(Swertia perennis)*, Fig. 232, grows in deep, wet soil and has an erect single stem about 1 foot high from a slender rootstalk. It is an alpine plant that grows in elevations from 8,000 to 10,000 feet high. It blooms in late summer with racemes of flowers that are greenish white tinged with violet blue. Swertias were named for the Dutch botanist Emanuel Sweert.

Fig. 233. Buckbean

BUCKBEAN FAMILY

BUCKBEAN *(Menyanthes trifoliata)*, Fig. 233, grows in the high Uintas in bogs and on the margins of alpine lakes. It has a thick rootstalk with membranous sheathing on the stem. The flowers come in racemes of 10 to 20 blossoms on scapes 4 to 12 inches high. Each blossom is about ¾ inch across and is smooth and white on the outside and pinkish with short scales that extend into the tube. They bloom from June to August.

Fig. 234. Milkweed

MILKWEED FAMILY

MILKWEED *(Asclepias cryptoceras)*, Fig. 234, is a low, prostrate plant that grows in loose, gravelly soil on the south slopes of the Uinta Mountains. The flowers are usually borne in a terminal umbel or in vigorous plants, with a second umbel at the node below. The blossoms are greenish yellow and about an inch across. It blooms in May and June. The seed pod is typical of the milkweed family.

SHOWY MILKWEED (*Asclepias speciosa*), Fig. 235, is our common and beautiful milkweed that grows 3 to 4 feet tall on stream banks and in moist meadows. Its sturdy, branching stems and tough, thick leaves are pubescent and gray green. The blossoms are 1 inch across, thick petaled and pale pink. They have a soft, frosted texture. It blooms in June and the seeds mature in September. This planṫ is a favorite host of the larval stage of the tiger-swallowtail butterfly. The thick, milky sap, which is present in all parts of the plant, gives it its common name. *A. incarnata* is very similar but is smaller.

Fig. 235. Showy Milkweed

PHLOX FAMILY

COLLOMIA (*Collomia grandiflora*), Fig. 236, is found growing under trees in our mountains. It is an erect plant, 1 to 2 feet high, with tight clusters of flowers at the top of the stem and in the axils of the leaves. The leaves are dark green and shiny, with a light center vein. The blossoms are tubular, which is typical of the phlox family. The corolla is about 1 inch long and an unusual apricot color. The stamens are blue. The seeds develop a mucilaginous coat when they are wet.

Fig. 236. Collomia

COLLOMIA (*Collomia linearis*), Fig. 237, grows in moist to medium dry soil in open places in our mountains from 5,000 up to about 8,000 foot elevations. They are generally unbranched and smaller than *C. grandiflora*. The blossoms are ¼ to ½ inches long, lilac to dark pink and are usually confined to the top of the stem. It blooms in June and July.

Fig. 237. Collomia

Fig. 238. Scarlet Gilia

SCARLET GILIA *(Gilia aggregata)*, Fig. 238, is a 20 inch, biennial with a single stem that later branches at the terminals. It is heavily foliated at the base of the plant with fleshy, coarsely pubescent leaves. The blossoms are scarlet to coral and are frequently spotted with yellow and white. It has a distinctly skunky odor. It blooms from June to September and can be found at middle elevations throughout our mountains. This plant is a favorite with humming birds.

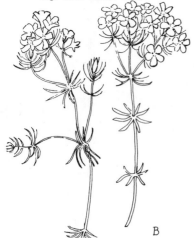

Fig. 239. Feather Gilia

FEATHER GILIA *(Linanthus nuttallii)*, Fig. 239, is an erect, showy perennial found on dry, gravelly hillsides at high altitudes. It grows in thick clumps, often a foot in diameter, and 5 to 8 inches high from a woody base. Its leaves are needle-like, shiny and green. The blossoms, which come in June, July and August, are pure white to creamy yellow.

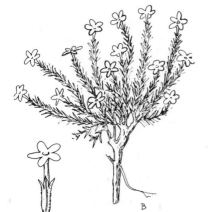

Fig. 240. Hoods, Phlox

HOODS PHLOX *(Phlox hoodii)*, Fig. 240, grows on dry, rocky slopes at middle to high elevations. It forms a compact clump 6 to 8 inches broad and 5 inches high. The leaves are sharp pointed and woolly pubescent. The blossoms come from April to July and are bright lilac to white. The old leaves cling to the stems and new growth as well as blossoms to terminal. It grows throughout our area.

WILD PHLOX *(Phlox longifolia)*, Fig. 241, is a low branching perennial with a creeping rootstock and opposite leaves. The leaves are gray green, soft to the touch and lightly pubescent. It grows on our open foothills, wherever the soil is relatively lime-free. It frequently occurs in large, compact patches and in May produces myriads of clear pink or sometimes white blossoms.

Fig. 241. Wild Phlox

WHITE POLEMONIUM *(Polemonium foliosissimum* or *P. albiflorum)*, Fig. 242, grows at middle elevations in our mountains. It inhabits areas where the soil is rich and either damp or medium dry. The mature plant is a dense clump, made up of leafy stems about 2 feet high. The leaves and stems are a fresh, light green and are softly pubescent. Its blossoms are each about 1 inch in diameter and are white with yellow stamens. They have a slight skunky odor and are at their height of bloom in June and July.

Fig. 242. White Polemonium

WESTERN POLEMONIUM *(Polemonium occidentale)*, Fig. 243, is an erect plant with slender stems 1 to 3 feet tall, from strong, creeping rootstocks. The leaves are more distinctly divided than *P. foliosissimum* and are slightly sticky. It grows in wet places at lower elevations in our mountains and blooms from June to September. The blossoms are lavender blue with a white base. The orange stamens are inserted half way up the corolla tube. The whole plant has a skunky odor.

Fig. 243. Western Polemonium

Fig. 244. Sky Pilot

SKY PILOT, STICKY POLE-MONIUM *(Polemonium viscosum)*, Fig. 244, grows at high altitudes in lime-free soil. Its erect clumps are 12 to 20 inches high with the flowers at the top of the stem. The leaves are mostly basal and with crowded leaflets arranged in whorls. The flowers are blue or occasionally white with orange stamens. The whole plant has a strong skunky odor which adheres enduringly to everything it touches.

WATERLEAF FAMILY

HESPEROCHIRON *(Hesperochiron pumilus)*, Fig. 245, is a delightful spring flowering plant that can be found in high mountain meadows. It is only 2 to 4 inches high with basal leaves that are thick and smooth. The delicate blossoms appear on scapes and are about an inch in diameter. They are white with yellow at the base and are marked with fine black lines. The stamens are hairy at the base.

Fig. 245. Hesperochiron

Fig. 246. Water Leaf

WATERLEAF *(Hydrophyllum capitatum)*, Fig. 246, is a tender, crisp, erect herb that grows 4 to 12 inches tall. In our area it can be found growing in damp, rich soil in open woods in the northern end of our state. It has a short rhizome with short, thickish roots. The stems and leaves are softly pubescent. It blooms in April and May with pale lavender or whitish blossoms in compact heads 1 to 2 inches in diameter. The corollas are tissue thin, tubular, and have exserted stamens. *H. occidentale* is very similar, with longer stems and looser blossoms. They grow in oak woods from Ogden south to Mount Nebo.

Phacelia is a Greek name meaning cluster. It belongs to an interesting group of plants that are numerous in our area. In this genus, there are more than a hundred species, most of them native to the western United States. VIRGATE PHACELIA *(Phacelia heterophylla)*, Fig. 247, is a biennial that in our area grows 1 or 2 feet high on dry, gravelly mountainsides. The stems and leaves are gray green and harshly pubescent, often irritating to the skin. The delicate blossoms are lavender with white styles and brownish anthers. They bloom from May to July.

Fig. 247. Virgate Phacelia

THREADLEAF PHACELIA or SAND PHACELIA *(Phacelia linearis)*, Fig. 248, is an annual that usually has a single erect stem less than 1 foot tall, and several blossoms at the top. The leaves and stem are pubescent and grayish green. They bloom in May and June with lavender flowers that are marked with dark lines.

Fig. 248. Threadleaf Phacelia

SILVERLEAF PHACELIA *(Phacelia leucophylla)*, Fig. 249, is so named because the foliage is densely covered with harsh silvery gray pubescence. It grows on gravelly hillsides in our mountains and blooms in June and July. Its habit of growth is interesting. As they bloom, the stems "uncurl", becoming straight-stemmed at maturity. The blossoms are white to pale lavender, about 1/4 inch long and have the texture of thin tissue paper.

Fig. 249. Silverleaf Phacelia

Fig. 250. Silky Phacelia

SILKY PHACELIA *(Phacelia sericea)*, Fig. 250, is a perennial that grows in the Uinta Mountains. From a woody root crown, it produces erect stems 8 to 16 inches tall. It blooms from June to August with dense spikes of lavender purple flowers with protruding stamens. The leaves are silvery pubescent and silky.

Fig. 251. Little Cryptantha

BORAGE FAMILY

LITTLE CRYPTANTHA *(Cryptantha nana)*, Fig. 251, grows on dry, sandy hillsides and blooms in May and June. Its 6 inch high stems arise from a sturdy root stalk. The leaves and stems are densely pubescent and gray green. Its flowers, like other members of the borage family, have a fused corolla. They are white with a yellow center. The calyx lobes are as long as the corolla. *C. flavoculata* closely resembles *C. nana* but is twice as tall and has larger flowers. The calyx lobes are shorter than the petals.

Fig. 252. Hound's Tongue

HOUND'S TONGUE *(Cynoglossum officinale)*, Fig. 252, is a stout, erect, leafy plant, 2 feet tall. It is a native of Europe and Asia that has become well established all over the United States. Its leaves and stems are grayish green and soft pubescent. It blooms in May and June with dark maroon-red flowers each slightly less than ½ inch across. The seeds are covered with short, barbed prickles.

STICKSEED *(Hackelia patens)*, Fig. 253, is a common plant on our foothills in May and June. It grows about 2 feet high with a few erect or ascending branches growing from the base. The forget-me-not-like blossoms are white marked with blue. *H. jessicae* closely resembles it but has blue flowers marked with white. They both have nutlets armed with short, barbed prickles which give them their common name.

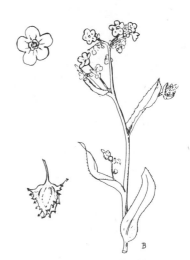

Fig. 253. Stickseed

STONESEED *(Lithospermum incisum)*, Fig. 254, has many leafy stems growing 1 to 2 feet tall from a woody crown. The bright yellow blossoms begin blooming in May and continue through most of June. The first flowers are fringed and about 1 inch in diameter; later ones are smaller and lighter in color. They grow on dry slopes in elevations between 4,500 to 8,500 feet.

Fig. 254. Stoneseed

STONESEED *(Lithospermum ruderale)*, Fig. 255, grows on foothills and in open fields over most of our area. The 10 to 12 inch branching stems have numerous soft pubescent leaves and terminal blossoms that are creamy to yellowish green in color. It blooms in May and June. This plant is the source of the drug most commonly used in oral contraceptives. *L. multiflorm* resembles *L. ruderale* but is more slender with blossoms set in less foliage. The roots contain a deep purple dye that was used by the Indians.

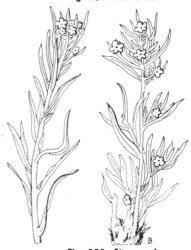

Fig. 255. Stoneseed

Fig| 256. Shortstyle Bluebells

SHORTSTYLE BLUEBELLS *(Mertensia brevistyla)*, Fig. 256, is easily mistaken for forget-me-nots. Its blossoms are the intense blue typical of *Mertensia* species but it does not have the long corolla or nodding habit associated with most species in this genus. It grows on dry hillsides at elevations between 5,000 and 10,500 feet. The stems are 4 to 14 inches tall with terminal flower heads that become more open as it matures. It blooms in April and May.

Fig. 257. Mountain Bluebells

MOUNTAIN BLUEBELLS *(Mertensia ciliata)*, Fig. 257, is an erect or ascending plant with stems 1 to 3 feet tall. It grows at altitudes between 5,000 and 12,000 feet. The leaves are smooth with pubescence on the margins. The blossoms are ½ inch or more long, bell-like, nodding and blue with tinges of pink. They grow on stream banks and at the edge of meadows where they form thick stands. This is perhaps the handsomest of the *Mertensias*.

Fig. 258. Bluebells

BLUEBELLS *(Mertensia oblongifolia)*, Fig. 258, is a compact, erect, leafy plant that grows on sagebrush hills and is rarely more than 1 foot high. The leaves are thick and dark green with a bluish bloom. The name *oblongifolia* refers to the shape of the leaves. The blossoms are bright clear blue and nodding. They bloom in April and May.

VERBENA FAMILY

BLUE VERBENA *(Verbena hastata)*, Fig. 259, grows on ditch banks and wet places in fields. It has one or two erect, leafy stems 16 to 32 inches high from each root. Its densely flowered spikes bloom with a few blue flowers at a time, from May to September.

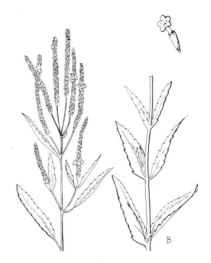

Fig. 259. Blue Verbena

MINT FAMILY

HORSE MINT *(Agastache urticifolia)*, Fig. 260, belongs to a family of aromatic herbs and shrubs with opposite leaves and, square stems that is widely distributed throughout our area. This is an erect, branching, hollow stemmed perennial 3 to 6 feet high with several stems from each root. It blooms in July and August with dense cymes of pale-pink blossoms that are either delightfully aromatic or unpleasantly scented, depending entirely upon personal taste. It is quite common in our canyons where it adapts to both wet and dry situations.

Fig. 260. Horse Mint

HOREHOUND *(Marrubium vulgare)*, Fig. 261, is another mint imported from Europe and Asia that has become well established here. It grows in clumps 12 to 18 inches high on road sides and in fields. The gray-green leaves and stems are woolly pubescent and have a rag-like texture. The flowers are small, white and grow in dense axillary clusters. It blooms from May to August. The leaves were used as a flavoring for the horehound candy that was so popular in Utah's pioneer colonies. *Marrubium* is from Hebrew and means bitter.

Fig. 261. Horehound

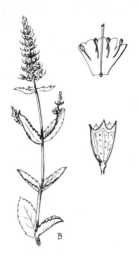

Fig. 262. Spearmint

SPEARMINT *(Mentha spicata)*, Fig. 262, is native to Europe and naturalized over most of America. It is prized for the aromatic flavor of its leaves. It grows in pure stands in damp places and on stream banks. In our area it rarely grows more than 2 feet high and has strong and prolific rootstalks. The pale lavender flowers are small but quite attractive. It blooms in June and July.

Fig. 263. Mountain Pennyroyal

MOUNTAIN PENNYROYAL *(Monardella odoratissima)*, Fig. 263, grows on hillsides and talus slopes high in our mountains. It grows in showy clumps usually not more than 1 foot high but frequently spreading twice that wide. The rose-lavender blossoms come in tight terminal heads, subtended by showy bracts. The whole plant is pleasantly aromatic when crushed. In July and August, when this plant is in bloom, it is one of the most attractive of our wild flowers.

Fig. 264. Catnip

CATNIP *(Nepeta cataria)*, Fig. 264, has erect, hollow stems and soft pubescent leaves that are aromatic. It grows to about 3 feet high in moist places and has terminal and axillary cymes of white or pale lavender blossoms spotted with purple. It is a native of Europe that was introduced into our area by early pioneers to whom it was an important medication for colic and related ills. This is the catnip that is sold in pet stores.

FIGWORT FAMILY

Castillejas are probably the most conspicuous species of plants we have in this area. EARLY INDIAN PAINT BRUSH *(Castilleja chromosa)*, Fig. 265, is one of the most colorful. It grows in upright clumps 8 to 16 inches high in dry, gravelly soil and blooms in May and June with dense terminal spikes. The blossoms are rather inconspicuous, but they are surrounded with brilliant red bracts. The leaves are very pubescent and gray green in color. *Castillejas* can grow independently but are usually parasitic on the roots of other plants. The Indians used the roots of *Castilleja* as an ingredient in making black dye for buckskin. *C. linariaefolia* closely resembles *C. chromosa* but has narrower, grass-like leaves and exserted flowers.

Fig. 265. Early Indian Paint Brush

INDIAN PAINT BRUSH *(Castilleja rhexifolia)*, Fig. 266, has erect stems 12 to 20 inches high with long, almost glabrous leaves. The flowering heads are purple red. *C. miniata* is taller with scarlet-red flowers and may be branched near the top. It is otherwise similar to *C. rhexifolia*.

Fig. 266. Indian Paint Brush

BLUE-EYED MARY *(Collinsia parviflora)*, Fig. 267, is less important for its size or appearance than its numbers. It is a small annual from 2 to 6 inches tall with blue and white irregular blossoms ⅛ to ¼ inch long. It frequently forms thick stands in open areas where it germinates, flowers and matures seed in early spring before the winter moisture is out of the ground.

Fig. 267. Blue-Eyed Mary

Fig. 268. Butter and Eggs

BUTTER AND EGGS—TOAD-FLAX *(Linaria vulgaris)*, Fig. 268, is a vigorous, erect perennial that grows in clumps with stiff, straight stems usually 12 to 14 inches tall. Its flowers are rich yellow, irregular, spurred and heavily perfumed. It is native to Eurasia and is common in open, damp areas all over America. It blooms all summer.

Fig. 269. Monkey Flower

MONKEY FLOWER *(Mimulus guttatus)*, Fig. 269, is a tender, creeping, decumbent perennial that grows in stream beds and meadows throughout our mountains. Its crisp leaves and stems were used as salads by early miners and white settlers. The yellow blossoms with cinnamon-colored spots are reminiscent of little faces which accounts for the name *Mimulus*, Latin for comic actor. The blossoms are an inch long and nearly as wide with irregular corolla and bearded lower lip. The stems are 1 to 3 feet long with leaves and blossoms distributed over most of their length.

Fig. 270. Lewis Monkey Flower

LEWIS MONKEY FLOWER *(Mimulus lewisii)*, Fig. 270, is the largest of all species of *Mimulus*. It is sometimes 3 feet high with blossoms nearly 1½ inches across. The flowers are rose magenta with yellow throat and stamens. It grows in rich wet ground in our mountains.

PRIMROSE MONKEY FLOW-ER *(Mimulus primuloides)*,´ Fig. 271, grows in moist places, often in moss banks in the Uinta mountains. Its roots are frequently stoloniferous but not always. It produces three veined, basal leaves and single blossoms on 5 inch scapes. The flowers, about an inch long and ¾ inch wide, are yellow with three brown spots on the lower petals. It blooms from July to September.

Fig. 271. Primrose Monkey Flower

TOLMIE OWLCLOVER *(Orthocarpus tolmiei)*, Fig. 272, is a slender plant with wiry pubescent stems and slender, gray-green leaves. The inconspicuous flowers have clear bright yellow bracts. It blooms in late summer. *O. luteus* is very similar but is generally unbranched and has dark-green leaves that dry blackish. Both species grow in drying meadows and hillsides.

Fig. 272. Tolmie Owlclover

LOUSE-WORT *(Pedicularis racemosa)*, Fig. 273, is a branching compact plant 16 to 20 inches high with many leafy racemes of white, irregular flowers. The leaves have finely toothed margins and are glabrous. It can be found in moist, open coniferous forests at elevations between 6,000 and 9,500 feet throughout our area. It blooms in July and August. *P. parryi* has ferny leaves and straight, 20 inch racemes of flowers. The blossoms are a little smaller and more hooded than *P. racemosa*.

Fig. 273. Louse-Wort

Fig. 274. Elephant's Head

ELEPHANT'S HEAD (*Pedicularis groenlandica*), Fig. 274, is one of the most interesting plants in our flora. The leaves, which are mostly basal, are ferny and dark green. The flower stems grow about 1 foot high and bear ¼ inch blossoms that look exatly like little magenta-pink elephant heads. They grow in damp areas in alpine elevations. They bloom in July and August.

Fig. 275. Blue Penstemon

BLUE PENSTEMON (*Penstemon cyananthus*), Fig. 275, grows on dry, gravelly hillsides and blooms from May through July on the Wasatch Mountains and the Bear River Range. Each plant produces several 2 to 3 foot stems of magnificent blue flowers. It is a primary invader, being among the first plants to grow in disturbed areas. *P. cyananthus* ssp. *compactus* is shorter, has a woody base and narrower leaves. The blossoms are a little longer and the same blue color.

Fig. 276. Low Penstemon

LOW PENSTEMON (*Penstemon humilus*), Fig. 276, produces masses of spectacular color on dry hillsides, roadway cuts and mountain slopes from May to July. It grows in many-stemmed clumps 4 to 12 inches high. The blossoms are about ½ inch long and every shade of blue from lavender to light sky blue. *P. leonardi* is much like *P. humilus* but is a sturdier, more compact plant with thicker stems and broader blossoms.

WHIPPLE'S PENSTEMON *(Penstemon whippleanus)*, F i g. 277, is dark purple or wine colored with white stripes in the throat. The lower lip projects and is covered with long white hair. It grows on rocky slopes at high elevations and blooms in July and August. The plant is usually about a foot high but may be less at very high altitudes.

Fig. 277. Whipple's Penstemon

HARE FIGWORT *(Scrophularia lanceolata)*, Fig. 278, received its common name from the supposed resemblance of its blossoms to members of the rabbit family. The plant is open, erect, branching and often 5 feet tall. The blossoms are brown and pale green with maroon markings at the base. It forms thick stands on stream banks and in moist woods in our canyons and blooms from May to July.

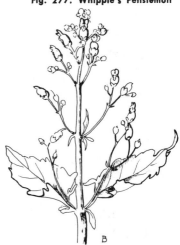

Fig. 278. Hare Figwort

KITTEN TAIL *(Synthyris pinnatifida)*, Fig. 279, in our area is found only in the high areas of the Bear River Range at the northern end of our state. It grows on gravelly alpine summits where it blooms in July only a few feet from the melting snow banks. The flowers are dark blue and come in racemes 3 inches high before their leaves appear. The leaves are basal and have a ferny texture.

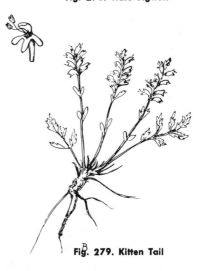

Fig. 279. Kitten Tail

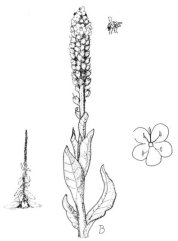
Fig. 280. Flanel Mullein

FLANNEL MULLEIN *(Verbascum thapsus)*, Fig. 280, is another widely naturalized plant that is native to Europe. It is common on road sides and in fields. The thick gray-green leaves are covered with a star-shaped pubescence that gives them a flannel-like texture. This is interesting to look at under a hand lens. The single flower stalks are often more than 6 feet tall, with bright yellow blossoms that bloom a few at a time at the top.

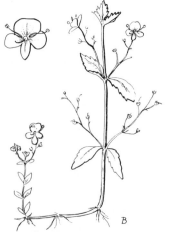
Fig. 281. Speedwell

SPEEDWELL *(Veronica americana)*, Fig. 281, is a semi-aquatic plant found in rich, wet soil up to about 10,000 feet. It is a glabrous and erect or ascending plant with stems 4 to 40 inches long. The blossoms are in axillary racemes, usually blooming a few at a time. They are blue violet marked with darker lines and a little less than ½ inch wide. *V. wormskjoldii* is not aquatic but grows in damp, alpine meadows. The blossoms are darker and a little smaller than *V. americana* and it is pubescent.

BLADDERWORT FAMILY

COMMON BLADDERWORT *(Utricularia vulgaris)*, Fig. 282, is an aquatic with all but the blossoms submersed. The thread-like, finely dissected leaves have small, translucent bladders that serve to float the plant as well as being traps that capture and absorb small insects. Most of the nitrogen used by the plant is acquired in this way. The blossoms are about ¾ inch across and yellow with brown markings.

Fig. 282. Common Bladderwort

PLANTAIN FAMILY

(Plantago lanceolata), Fig. 283, is a common plant in moist, grassy places. It is a biennial or perennial with a fibrous root and large linear veined, basal leaves. The flowers come in single spikes 6 to 20 inches long that bloom from the base upward. *P. eriopoda* is similar but smaller and with less compact flower spikes. *P. major* has broader leaves but a very similar blossom spike.

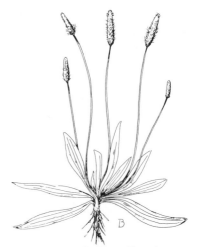

Fig. 283. Buckhorn Plantain

PURSH'S PLANTAIN *(Plantago purshii)*, Fig. 284, is an annual with gray green, very pubescent stems and leaves. The white blossoms are delicate, tissue thin and semi-transparent. The flower spikes are borne on 2 to 6 inch scapes. It grows on dry hillsides throughout our mountains.

Fig. 284. Pursh's Plantain

MADDER FAMILY

CATCHWEED BEDSTRAW *(Galium aparine)*, Fig. 285, has slender, weak stems 6 to 40 inches long that are erect or climbing on other plants. It is an inconspicuous plant with small white blossoms growing from the upper axils. The leaves and stems are densely covered with small hooked bristles that affix themselves so firmly to clothing or fur that the whole plant is frequently uprooted. It grows at the edges of wood land and thickets and blooms from March to August. The fruits are double and bristled.

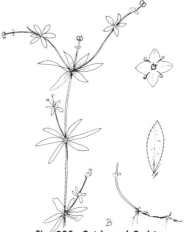

Fig. 285. Catchweed Bedstraw

Fig. 286. Northern Bedstraw

NORTHERN BEDSTRAW (*Galium boreale*), Fig. 286, is an erect, branching plant 12 to 18 inches high that produces dense clusters of small white flowers at the ends of the branches. The stems are square with four leaves in a whorl at the nodes. It grows on the borders of mountain meadows and open woods and blooms all summer. *Galium* is a Greek word meaning milk—from the use of some species in curdling milk. *Galium* roots were used by Indians as an ingredient in making dye.

VALERIAN FAMILY

Fig. 287. Edible Valerian

EDIBLE VALERIAN (*Valeriana edulis*), Fig. 287, is a robust perennial with erect stems 4 inches to somewhat over 3 feet high. The leaves are mostly basal, thick, parallel veined and glabrous. They grow in moist woods at lower and middle elevations in our area. The flowers bloom from May to September with numerous small yellow to greenish blossoms. The roots are thick and have a foul odor. Even so, they are said to have been cooked and used as food by some tribes of Indians.

Fig. 288. Wild Heliotrope

WILD HELIOTROPE (*Valeriana occidentalis*), Fig. 288, has stems 1 to 2 feet high with terminal clusters of small white, fragrant blossoms. The stems arise from slender rhizomes and the pinnately veined leaves are thinner than in the above species. It grows in our high mountain areas in meadows and in moist open woods.

TEASEL FAMILY

TEASEL *(Dipsacus sylvestris)*, Fig. 289, is a native of Europe naturalized over most of America. It is a stout biennial with rough, prickly stems and leaves. In our area it grows about 3 feet high in solid stands in moist or wet areas. The lavender flowers are less conpicuous than the ridged spiny scales and bracts that make up the flower head. They turn brown and remain intact long after the plant is dead. These dried heads have numerous small hooks that for centuries have made them valuable as fine brushes in the wool and tailoring industry. The florist industry still uses them extensively for winter bouquets.

Fig. 289. Teasel

BELLFLOWER FAMILY

There are two campanulas that grow on dry, rocky slopes in the Uinta Mountains and are easily confused. PARRY'S BELLFLOWER *(Campanula parryi)*, Fig. 290, grows 6 to 12 inches high with slender, unbranched stems. Its rather sparse leaves are glabrous except on the edges. It blooms with single, nodding blue lavender blossoms at the ends of the stems.

Fig. 290. Parry's Bellflower

BLUEBELL *(Campanula rotundifolia)*, Fig. 291, has branching stems that grow 4 inches to 3 feet tall with terminal blossoms on each. Its round basal leaves frequently disappear before it blooms. The stem leaves are grass-like. The blossoms of both species vary in size from about ½ inch long to more than an inch.

Fig. 291. Bluebell

Fig. 292. Yarrow

SUNFLOWER FAMILY

YARROW *(Achillea millefolium)*, Fig. 292, is a highly variable perennial that is common throughout our area. It has stiff, erect, branching stems 12 to 30 inches high and soft, ferny leaves that are mostly basal. The flowers are borne in flat-topped panicles and are white, grayish or rarely pink, all with yellow centers. The leaves and flowers are very aromatic. In past centuries this plant has been highly valued for its supposed medical properties.

Fig. 293. Mountain Dandelion

MOUNTAIN DANDELION *(Agoseris glauca)*, Fig. 293, is an erect, sturdy perennial 4 to 18 inches high that grows from a heavy taproot and crown. The flowers are about 1½ inches across and yellow with dark brush-stroke markings on the back. The petals are finely toothed on the edge. It grows on hillsides and around mountain meadows at lower elevations in our area. *A glauca* var. *parviflora* is similar but grows at higher altitudes.

Fig. 294. Pearly Everlasting

PEARLY EVERLASTING *(Anaphalis margaritacea)*, Fig. 294, is distinguished by its pearly white, papery bracts that surround the rather inconspicuous yellow blossoms and hold their shape even when dried. The leaves and stems are covered with a white woolly pubescence that gives them a silvery appearance. It grows in clumps 1 to 3 feet high on dry to moist mountain sides in rocky soil. They bloom in June, July and August.

ROSE PUSSYTOES *(Antennaria rosea)*, Fig. 295, grows in poor, gravelly soil on high mountain ridges, slopes and in drying meadows. It is 2 to 12 inches high with gray woolly pubescent leaves and stems. The individual flowers are about ⅛ inch across and are made up of pink or white scaly bracts with a white pappus center. It blooms in June and July. *A dimorpha* has a similar habit of growth but is usually less than 2 inches high and forms dense, gray mats on rocky foothills in April and May.

Fig. 295. Rose Pussytoes

MAYWEED — CHAMOMILE *(Anthemis cotula)*, Fig. 296, is an European plant that was introduced into this country many years ago and now is naturalized over wide areas. It is a leafy, much branched annual that grows 4 to 10 inches high in disturbed areas and along road sides. It blooms from May to September with white blossoms an inch in diameter.

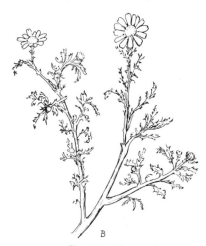

Fig. 296. Mayweed

BURDOCK *(Arctium minus)*, Fig. 297, is an erect, branching plant 6 to 8 feet high with leaves up to 10 inches across and 12 inches long. The magenta pink and white blossoms are tubular and are surrounded by hooked bracts that, with maturity, become troublesome burs that are painful to skin and all but impossible to remove from hair. The leaves and blossom heads have a thin woolly pubescence and a slightly bitter odor. They grow in rich, moist soil at the mouth of our canyons and bloom in August and September. This plant was introduced from Europe and Asia.

Fig. 297. Burdock

Fig. 298. Meadow Arnica

MEADOW ARNICA *(Arnica chamissonis)*, Fig. 298, grows from long rhizomes. It has erect stems 1 to 3 feet high with five pairs of leaves and usually three flowers to a stem. The blossoms are 2 inches across and dark lemon yellow. The leaves are glandular pubescent. It grows in mountain meadows and on moist hillsides. *A. mollis* closely resembles *A. chamissonis* but usually has only three pairs of leaves. Both species are distributed throughout our area. Both bloom in June, July and August.

Fig. 299. Hearleafed Arnica

HEARTLEAFED ARNICA *(Arnica cordifolia)*, Fig. 299, has abundant, fibrous rhizomes that connect pure stands of single, unbranched plants that are 1 to 2 feet high. They grow in open woods, frequently in pine and spruce forests and bloom from May to August. The blossoms are solid yellow, 2½ to 3 inches in diameter and are terminal with one flower to a stem. The name *cordifolia* refers to the heart-shaped leaves. They are slightly rough, glandular and gray green. It is distributed throughout our area.

Fig. 300. Mountain Arnica

MOUNTAIN ARNICA *(Arnica latifolia)*, Fig. 300, is a perennial from a slender scaly rhizome. It grows 4 to 24 inches high and has three or sometimes more blossoms 1¼ inches across. It grows in moist open places in our mountains, usually at medium to low elevations. It blooms from June to August.

ARNICA *(Arnica sororia)*, Fig. 301, is a slender, narrow leaved plant 2 feet or more high. It grows on dry foothills and at moderate elevations in the Bear River Range in northern Utah. *A. fulgens* is very similar but is sturdier and has a dense tuft of tawny hair at the crown. It grows in the Uinta Mountains. Both plants bloom from May to July.

Asters are showy and beautiful. They closely resemble fleabane daisies *(Erigeron,* page 127) and are frequently confused with them. They differ mostly in the type of bracts they have beneath the flower heads. Asters have several rows of bracts while *Erigeron* species usually have one or two rows. Most *Erigerons* also have narrower, more numerous ray flowers. HOARY ASTER *(Aster canescens)*, Fig. 302, grows in clumps 1 to 2 feet high from a taproot. The stems are much branched and have numerous violet-colored blossoms 1½ inches in diameter. The leaves are toothed and slightly spiney. *A. chilensis* ssp. *adscendens* is similar but is often twice as tall and has larger leaves with smooth margins. It grows in moist situations at lower elevations than *A. canescens*. The blossoms are blue or white. They both bloom from July to September.

EATON'S ASTER *(Aster eatonii)*, Fig. 303, has numerous erect or ascending branches up to 40 inches tall. From July to September they are covered with masses of whitish blossoms, each a little more than an inch in diameter. The leaves are thin with a heavy midvein. It grows on stream banks at middle elevations.

Fig. 301. Arnica

Fig. 302. Hoary Aster

Fig. 303. Eaton's Aster

Fig. 304. Leafy Aster

LEAFY ASTER *(Aster folia-ceus)*, Fig. 304, grows 10 to 20 inches tall in damp places at elevations between 6,000 and 10,000 feet. It has four to six flower heads to each stem, each 1¾ to 2 inches in diameter. They are distinguished by the leafy bracts at the base of the flower. The disk flowers, in the center of the flower, are yellow and the ray flowers (resembling petals) are deep violet. It blooms from July to September.

Fig. 305. Balsamroot

BALSAMROOT *(Balsamorhiza macrophylla)*, Fig. 305, grows in vigorous clumps 18 inches to 2 feet high on dry, rocky hillsides. It blooms in May with numerous 5 inch golden-yellow terminal blossoms. The large, deeply cut basal leaves are green, softly pubescent and have a slightly unpleasant medical odor. The stems and bracts have long, tangled pubescence.

Fig. 306. Arrowleaf Balsamroot

ARROWLEAVED BALSAM-ROOT *(Balsamorhiza sagittata)*, Fig. 306, resembles *B. macrophylla* but has entire, gray green, heavily pubescent, arrow-shaped leaves. They frequently grow and bloom side by side. The Indians and later the Mormon Pioneers peeled away the outer layers of the thick, fleshy root and ate the center portion. Hence it was sometimes called "Mormon biscuit."

DOUGLAS PINCUSHION (*Chaenactis douglasii*), Fig. 307, is a perennial 18 to 24 inches high that can be found blooming on arid, rocky hillsides in June and July. The branching stems and ferny green leaves are covered with a white woolly, glandular pubescence. The flower heads, which are less than an inch long, contain 40 to 50 pinkish white, tubular flowers.

Fig. 307. Douglas Pincushion

GOLDEN ASTER (*Chrysopsis villosa*), Fig. 308, has stems 4 to 20 inches high from a woody taproot. The blossoms are terminal, a little less than an inch in diameter and golden yellow. The leaves are gray green and quite glandular pubescent. It grows in clumps on dry, gravelly hillsides and blooms from June to August.

Fig. 308. Golden Aster

CHICKORY (*Cichorium intybus*), Fig. 309, is a vigorous perennial with stiff, straight stems that in favored locations may be as much as 5 feet tall. In less favorable environment it grows only a few inches high. Both sized plants bear sky blue flower heads about 2 inches in diameter that bloom fresh each morning and fade by afternoon. Most of the leaves are basal and spreading. It was introduced from the Mediterranean area and has become widely naturalized in moist places on our roadsides and in lower canyons. A substitute and adulterant for coffee is sometimes made from the roots. It blooms from March to August.

Fig. 309. Chickory

Fig. 310. Elk Thistle

Fig. 311. Longleaf Hawksbeard

Fig. 312. Western Hawksbeard

ELK THISTLE *(Cirsium foliosum)*, Fig. 310, may be as much as 40 inches tall. It is unbranched, thick and leafy with terminal and some high, axillary blossoms. The leaves are dark green with light mid-veins and are abundantly armed with white spines. The blossoms are about 2 inches across and lavender pink with a lighter center. It grows in mountain meadows and blooms from May to September. A similar thistle is *Cirsium arvense* (CANADIAN THISTLE). It grows in large stands from creeping horizontal roots. It is 12 to 24 inches tall with purplish blossoms about 1 inch wide clustered at the top of the stems. It grows on dry, rocky mountain slopes.

LONG-LEAVED HAWKS-BEARD *(Crepis acuminata)*, Fig. 311, is a perennial 8 to 28 inches high that grows with sagebrush on dry canyon hillsides and blooms from May to August. The flower heads are terminal and have as many as 30 to 100 heads on a plant. The individual blossoms are ¾ inch across. Their petals are finely toothed on the ends.

WESTERN HAWKSBEARD *(Crepis occidentalis)*, Fig. 312, grows only 1 foot tall with individual yellow blossoms 1¼ inches in diameter. It is distinguished by stiff black hairs on the bracts. The leaves are gray green and covered with a fine pubescence. They have a tough elastic quality. It grows on rocky hillsides and blooms from May to July. It is sometimes confused with *Crepis runcinata* that has similar flowers, but may be nearly twice as tall with smaller, round tipped, shallowly notched leaves that are mostly basal. It grows in alkaline meadows.

CUTLEAVED DAISY *(Erigeron compositus)*, Fig. 313, grows on sandy banks on our foothills. Its leaves are mostly basal, green and glandular pubescent. It blooms in April, May and June with blossoms an inch or less in diameter on stems 4 to 10 inches high. The (center) disk flowers are yellow and tubular surrounded by pink, white or blue ray flowers. *Erigerons* or fleabane daisies are similar to Asters (page 123) and frequently have the same habitat and blooming season.

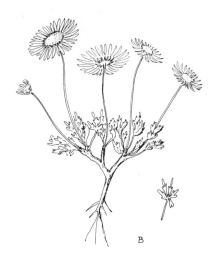

Fig. 313. Cutleaf Daisy

FLEABANE DAISY *(Erigeron leiomerus)*, Fig. 314, is a low alpine perennial with a long taproot and some low, sturdy branching stems. It grows on rocky places at high elevations. The blossoms are about an inch in diameter, deep blue or occasionally nearly white. They grow singly on stems 4 to 6 inches high and bloom in July and August. They are found throughout our area. This fleabane is sometimes confused with *E. ursinus* which is about the same size and grows in the same vicinity but has more slender pointed leaves and fibrous roots. The base of the stems on *E. ursinus* are dark reddish purple.

Fig. 314. Fleabane Daisy

HAIRY FLEABANE DAISY *(Erigeron pumilus)*, Fig. 315, is an attractive, round, much branched perennial plant with gray green silky pubescent stems and leaves. It usually grows about 12 inches tall and has numerous soft lavender to white blossoms from April to September. The round buds hang pendulant, but the blossoms are erect. It is a foothill plant associated with sagebrush.

Fig. 315. Hairy Fleabane Daisy

Fig. 316. Wandering Fleabane Daisy

Fig. 317. Showy Fleabane Daisy

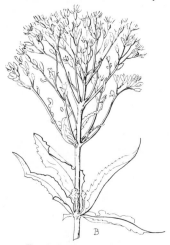

Fig. 318. Joe Pye Weed

WANDERING FLEABANE DAISY *(Erigeron peregrinus)*, Fig. 316, is one of the most beautiful of our fleabanes. It can be found on stream banks and in meadows at moderate to high elevations. It is fibrous rooted with short rhizomes. This is a highly variable species and may be only a few inches high or up to 2 feet or more. The heads are frequently solitary, or they may have several blossom heads on branches from one main stem. The ray flowers vary in color from pink through shades of violet blue and the heads are 1½ to 2 inches in diameter. It blooms in July and August.

SHOWY FLEABANE DAISY *(Erigeron speciosus)*, Fig. 317, is frequently confused with *E. peregrinus*. It is about the same size and has a similar habit of growth, but generally grows at lower elevations in wooded areas or on foothills. The leaves are more pointed than those of *E. peregrinus* and the ray flowers are narrower and more numerous. It blooms from June through August.

JOE PYE WEED *(Eupatorium maculatum)*, Fig. 318, has straight jointed stems 2½ to 3 feet high. The blossoms are terminal, dusty pink to purple and have a slightly offensive sweet fragrance. The coarsely veined leaves are in whorls of four or five each. It grows in wet meadows at lower elevations and blooms in summer. Joe Pye was an Indian medicine man in New England who earned fame for decoctions made from this plant.

WESTERN EUPATORIUM

(Eupatorium occidentale). Fig. 319, will be found in rocks by streams and lakes at middle elevations in our mountains. It grows on slender stems about 2½ feet tall from a woody base. The flower heads are about ½ inch long and range in color from cream to violet and scarlet. It blooms from July to September.

Fig. 319. Western Eupatorium

BLANKET FLOWER *(Gaillardia aristata)*, Fig. 320, has blossoms 2½ inches in diameter at the end of 8 to 24 inch stems. The rays are bicolored, yellow with red purple at the base. The stems and leaves are very pubescent and gray green with some reddish tones. It grows in open areas on the north and south slopes of the Uinta Mountains and blooms from May to September. It is frequently grown as a garden flower.

Fig. 320. Blanket Flower

GUM PLANT *(Grindelia squarrosa)*, Fig. 321, grows erect, branching clumps 1 to 2 feet high. The leaves and bracts are covered with a gummy, sticky substance with a resinous odor. It is native to the plains east of the Continental Divide, but has been widely introduced here. It is thought that the seeds affixed themselves to wagon wheels and were carried into this area with the early pioneers. It blooms July to September with solid yellow heads about 1¼ inches in diameter and can be found in dry areas by roadways and in open fields on our foothills.

Fig. 321. Gum Plant

Fig. 322. Stemless Goldenweed

STEMLESS GOLDENWEED *(Haplopappus acaulis)*, Fig. 322, is a spreading perennial that grows on dry, rocky ridges, mostly at high elevations in our mountains. It has a taproot with a crown that branches out for a foot or more. Its leaves are basal, coarse and pubescent. The heads are 1 to 1¼ inches across, golden yellow and borne singly on 4 to 6 inch scapes. It blooms from May to August.

Fig. 323. Lanceleaf Goldenweed

LANCELEAF GOLDENWEED *(Haplopappus lanceolatus)*, Fig. 323, grows in meadows and alkaline flats at elevations mostly above 7,000 feet. It has stems 10 to 20 inches high that curve upward and bear one to many yellow flower heads 1 to 1½ inches across. The leaves are thin, glabrous and have margins that vary from being smooth to deeply spiny toothed. Its blooming season is from May to August.

Fig. 324. Sneezeweed

SNEEZEWEED *(Helenium autumnale* var. *montanum)*, Fig. 324, grows in bottom lands and at the edge of marshes. It has stiff branching, leafy stems 6 to 32 inches high and in July and August numerous yellow heads about 1¼ inches across. The leaves are rough, pubescent, and attached to the stem for part of their length. They are thick and dull green with straw-colored veins.

LITTLE SUNFLOWER *(Helianthella uniflora)*, Fig. 325, is a perennial that has erect stems 10 to 48 inches high and grows in a clump. The leaves are coarse and rough to the touch. It blooms from May to August with bright yellow heads 1½ to 2½ inches across, usually one to a stem. It is found on dry canyon hillsides and in open aspen woods.

Fig. 325. Little Sunflower

COMMON SUNFLOWER *(Helianthus annuus)*, Fig. 326, is an annual that grows abundantly on foothills, roadsides and in open fields. It is one of the best known of American native flowers. It may be as much as 8 feet tall or as short as 1 foot, depending upon the opportunities offered by its environment. The leaves and stems are gray green, pubescent and have a sand-papery texture. The heads are 4 to 5 inches in diameter and are golden yellow and reddish brown. It has been introduced into Europe and Asia where it is extensively cultivated for its oily seed. It blooms from July to September.

Fig. 326. Common Sunflower

NUTTALL'S SUNFLOWER *(Helianthus nuttallii)*, Fig. 327, can be found on streambanks and in other moist places at lower to middle elevations. It is a perennial that grows in clumps 2 to 9 feet tall. The solid yellow heads are about 2½ inches across and bloom from August to November. The clusters of tuberous, thickened roots are characteristic of this particular plant.

Fig. 327. Nuttall's Sunflower

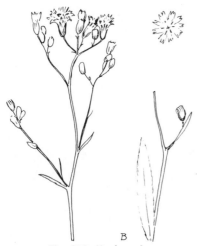

Fig. 328. Hawkweed

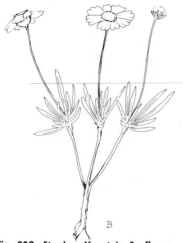

Fig. 329. Stemless Mountain Sunflower

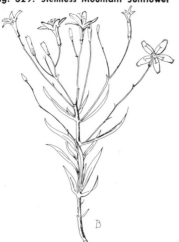

Fig. 330. Rushpink

HAWKWEED *(Hieracium scouleri)*, Fig. 328, is a highly variable species that grows in dry, gravelly soil in open woods high in our mountains. It has slender, erect stems 10 to 25 inches tall with bright yellow, terminal heads ¾ inch in diameter. The leaves are mostly basal, pubescent or glandular and gray green. They bloom from June to August. It contains a milky juice.

STEMLESS MOUNTAIN SUNFLOWER *(Hymenoxys acaulis)*, Fig. 329, has basal leaves growing from a branching crown and a woody taproot. The yellow flower heads are 1¾ inches wide and are borne at the top of 4 to 12 inch scapes. It grows on dry, rocky mountain ridges and slopes and blooms in May and June. *H. richardsonii* may be twice as tall and has leafy, branching stems. It is deadly poisonous to livestock. The blossoms are very similar in size and color to *H. acaulis*.

RUSHPINK or SKELETON PLANT *(Lygodesmia grandiflora)*, Fig. 330, is an erect perennial 6 to 20 inches high that inhabits dry, sandy or gravelly hillsides and blooms in May and June. The branches are wiry and somewhat reminiscent of candelabra in their arrangement. At the end of each there is a head of flowers 1¾ inches in diameter that opens in the morning and dies at sunset. Each of the ray flowers usually have five notches at the tip. The leaves and stems are gray green and have a milky-sticky juice.

PINEAPPLE WEED *(Matricaria matricarioides)*, Fig. 331, is usually only a few inches high and grows in thick stands along dry roadsides and in open places. It is branched from the base and has numerous ferny green leaves. It blooms in May and June with yellow green cones of disk flowers that look like daisies without ray flowers. When disturbed, they produce a scent that is reminiscent of pineapple. The blossom is spicy to the taste and quite palatable.

Fig. 331. Pineapple Weed

ROCK GOLDENROD *(Petradoria pumila)*, Fig. 332, is a low tufted perennial 6 to 10 inches high with numerous simple, erect, leafy stems. The leaves are light green and resinous. It blooms from July to October with numerous small yellow heads in clusters. It grows at elevations between 4,500 and 8,000 feet on dry, stony hillsides.

Fig. 332. Rock Goldenrod

WESTERN CONEFLOWER *(Rudbeckia occidentalis)*, Fig. 333, can be found growing at middle elevations along streams and in other moist places. It is frequently associated with aspen groves. The firm brown blossom head is about 2 inches long and comes at the top of erect, straight stems 1 to 6 feet tall. It is made up entirely of tubular disk flowers, the ray flowers being absent.

Fig. 333. Western Coneflower

Fig. 334. Woolly Butterweed

WOOLLY BUTTERWEED (*Senecio canus*), Fig. 334, is a 4 to 12 inch perennial with several erect stems and mostly basal, white, woolly pubescent leaves. The heads are yellow and ¾ to 1 inch across. They bloom from May to August and can be found in dry, rocky places from the foothills to above the timberline. The word *senecio* comes from the Latin word *senex*, referring to the pappus in the seeds.

Fig. 335. Mountain Butterweed

MOUNTAIN BUTTERWEED (*Senecio fremontii*), Fig. 335, is 4 to 6 inches high and freely branched from a decumbent base. The leaves are thickish, succulent and well distributed along the stem. The heads are yellow, 1 inch wide and come in July, August and September. They grow on rocky mountain sides at high elevations.

Fig. 336. Alkali Marsh Butterweed

ALKALI MARSH BUTTER-WEED (*Senecio hydrophilus*), Fig. 336, is a stout, erect, hollow-stemmed perennial that is 1 to 5 feet tall with numerous crowded terminal flower heads. The heads are yellow and ½ inch long. The bracts are green with dark markings on the tips. The leaves are glabrous, thick and dark green. They have a smooth, waxy surface. The roots are short, vertical rootstalks, crowded with fleshy roots. It grows in marshes and marshy places in our valleys and canyons up to about 8,500 feet. It is quite tolerant of salt and alkali and blooms from May to July.

GROUNDSEL *(Senecio integerrimus)*, Fig. 337, is a variable species that frequently resembles *S. hydrophilus* but has straighter, unbranched stems 18 to 28 inches tall. The yellow heads are about ¾ inch across. It becomes abundant in dry or moderately wet, open, disturbed places. The leaves are thick, glabrous and usually smooth edged at the base of the plant and dentate and pubescent above. They grow from the valleys to near timberline and bloom from May to July.

Fig. 337. Groundsel

ALPINE BUTTERWEED *(Senecio pauciflorus)*, Fig. 338, is a perennial 6 to 16 inches tall that grows in meadows and moist cliffs near the timberline. It blooms in July and August with orange-yellow or reddish terminal heads, each about an inch across when ray flowers are present. They are often missing. The leaves are thick and mostly glabrous. *S. pseudaureus* is a little taller, has relatively thin leaves that are more deeply toothed and broader at the base, tending to be cordate. The heads are about the same size, are lighter colored and in a tighter cluster. They bloom about the same time.

Fig. 338. Alpine Butterweed

TALL BUTTERWEED *(Senecio serra)*, Fig. 339, grows in clumps of several stems 2 to 6 feet tall. The numerous yellow heads are about ½ inch in diameter and have bracts that are usually black tipped. It grows in meadows and open places on our foothills and at moderate elevations. It blooms June to August.

Fig. 339. Tall Butterweed

Fig. 340. Meadow Goldenrod

Fig. 341. Wire Lettuce

Fig. 342. Common Dandelion

MEADOW GOLDENROD *(Solidago canadensis)*, Fig. 340, is common in our area. It has stems 1 to 6 feet high that grow from creeping rhizomes. The pale golden-yellow heads are small and numerous. It grows in meadows and in moist places in open woods at lower to middle elevations and blooms from July to October. *S. missouriensis* is very similar but reaches only 28 inches in height and grows in dry, open places. The leaves are broader at the tip than those of *S. canadensis*. It blooms from July to September. The name *Solidago* refers to its supposed healing properties.

WIRE LETTUCE *(Stephanomeria exigua)*, Fig. 341, grows on sandy hillsides. It is 4 to 24 inches tall with wire-like stems and narrow, pale-green leaves. It blooms from July to October with ½ inch heads that are pink with darker stamens. It has milky sap.

COMMON DANDELION *(Taraxacum officinale)*, Fig. 342, is one of our most familiar plants. It was introduced from Europe and has become well established over most of the United States. It is a stemless plant with numerous basal leaves and single blossom heads on round, hollow scapes that grow up to 12 inches tall. It has a long, thick taproot. It grows in moist places and blooms from April to October. HORNED DANDELION *(T. laevigatum)* is similar and grows at high altitudes in our mountains.

SALSIFY — OYSTER PLANT (*Tragopogon porrifolius*), Fig. 343, is a branching perennial with milky sap that was naturalized from Europe and now is common over most of the United States. It grows in clumps 2 to 4 feet high and has purple heads 3 inches in diameter that open in the morning and fade by noon. The fruiting head is dandelion-like, 3 inches in diameter and has a lustrous sheen that makes it very showy. It blooms from June to August. *T. dubius* is very similar but is a little shorter and has pale-yellow blossoms.

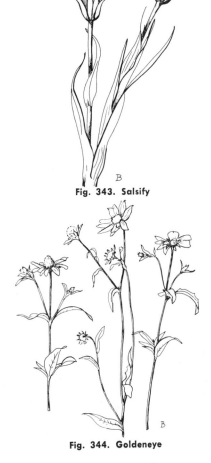

Fig. 343. Salsify

GOLDENEYE (*Viguiera multiflora*), Fig. 344, is one of the showiest plants in our canyons in August. It grows 1 to 3 feet high with numerous wiry, slender stems each of which is terminated with a golden-yellow head. It is found on dry slopes, roadsides and open forest from 4,500 to 11,000-foot elevation.

Fig. 344. Goldeneye

MULE EARS (*Wyethia amplexicaulis*), Fig. 345, can be found blooming on our gravelly foothills in May and June. It is a robust plant 2 to 3 feet high with large, shiny leaves and golden-yellow heads 4 inches in diameter. It is strongly aromatic and generally unpalatable to animals. It was named for Nathaniel J. Wyeth who collected it on the return trip of a western expedition in 1834.

Fig. 345. Mule Ears

PARASITES

AND

SAPROPHYTES

MISTLETOE FAMILY

WESTERN DWARF MISTLE-
TOE *(Arceuthobium campylopo-
da)*, Fig. 346, is the dense tufted
evergreen plant consisting of several forms. Different forms parasi-
tize different species of gymnosper-
ma. It has 2 to 4 inch, jointed
stems with swollen nodes. By specialized roots, it absorbs food from
the host plant. It apparently has no
cholorophyll and the scale-like
leaves are pale yellow or brownish.
The inconspicuous blossoms are followed by a one-seeded berry. *A.
douglasii* is similar but is smaller,
being only an inch or less tall and
is greenish yellow. It grows on
Pseudotsuga menziesii (DOUGLAS
FIR) and is inclined to be scattered along the host's stem.

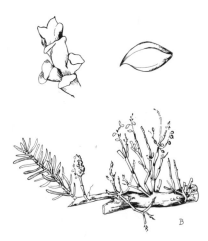

Fig. 346. Western Dwarf Mistletoe

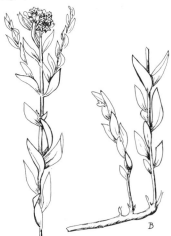

SANDALWOOD FAMILY

BASTARD TOADFLAX *(Co-
mandra umbellata)*, Fig. 347, is a
smooth, erect perennial herb 12 to
18 inches high that grows from a
woody base. It is semi-parasitic on
the roots of many species of plants.
It grows on our dry, gravelly hillsides and blooms with small pale
pink or lavender flowers in May
and June. Its leaves are smooth
and mostly pale green with pink
tinges.

Fig. 347. Bastard Toadflax

ORCHID FAMILY

Coral root orchids were so named
because of their fleshy, underground, brittle roots that resemble
coral. These plants lack chlorophyll
and, therefore, cannot manufacture
their own food. They get all of
their nourishment from decaying
vegetation in the deep shade of al-

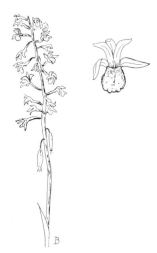

Fig. 348. Spotted Coral Root

Fig. 349. Corallorrhiza

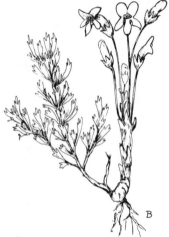

Fig. 350. Broomrape

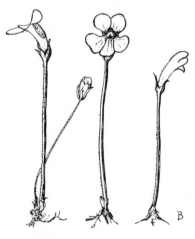

Fig. 351. Naked Broomrape

ders, spruces or aspen trees. Saprophytic plants, such as coral root orchids, live in a delicate equilibrium with fungi and dead organic matter. SPOTTED CORAL ROOT (*Corallorrhiza maculata*), Fig. 348, grows 8 to 20 inches high with single, erect stems with leaves that are reduced to three sheathing scales. The pinkish-tan flowers ½ to ¾ inches across have a lower lip that is white with cherry-red spots.

Corallorrhiza striata (Fig. 349) is very similar to *C. maculata* in habit of growth and size but the blossoms are different. They may be pink to purplish, marked with darker parallel lines or shades of clear yellow. Both species bloom from June to September.

BROOMRAPE FAMILY

BROOMRAPE (*Orobanche fasciculata*), Fig. 350, is a root parasite on several plants but is usually found on sagebrush (*Artemisia tridentata*). The enlarged base on the reddish stem completely encircles one of the lateral roots of the sagebrush. It depends entirely upon the host plant for food and water. Its scale-like leaves are tan with reddish tones and lack chlorophyll. It grows about 6 inches high with yellow to purple blossoms about ⅓ inch wide. It blooms from June to August.

NAKED BROOMRAPE (*Orobanche uniflora*), Fig. 351, grows 3 to 6 inches high in meadows and other damp places at low to moderate elevations. It is parasitic on several species of plants. Blooming time is from May to August with flowers that are purple to almost white.

INDEX

INDEX, continued

INDEX, continued

INDEX, continued